D0935386

THE GERMAN EUTHANASIA PROGRAM

EXCERPTS FROM

A Sign for Cain: An Explanation of Human Violence

FREDRIC WERTHAM, M.D.

HAYES PUBLISHING COMPANY, INC.
6304 Hamilton Avenue
Cincinnati, Ohio 45224
(513) 681-7559

Originally published as chapters 8 and 9 in *A Sign for Cain*
by The Macmillan Company of New York and Collier-
Macmillan Limited of London. Copyright 1966 by Fredric
Wertham. Paperback editions of *A Sign for Cain* were published by the Warner Paperback Library, New York, in 1969
and 1973. Reprinted with the permission of The Macmillan
Company, New York.

First Printing, January 1978

ISBN: 0-91728-10-0

Hayes Publishing Company, Inc.
6304 Hamilton Avenue
Cincinnati, Ohio 45224

Publisher's Foreword

To many Dr. Fredric Wertham's book, *A Sign for Cain,* has become a modern classic on the subject of violence. It has been read by millions and has given us all much to think about in this age of increasing violence. Chapters 8 and 9 describe with detailed documentation the Euthanasia Program that was conceived and carried out by German doctors from 1939 to 1945. The express purpose of this program was not to kill Jews, Gypsies, Poles, and other non-Aryans, but rather to purify the German race by the direct killing off of pure blooded German citizens who were physically, emotionally, or mentally defective.

This German Euthanasia Program preceded, by a full two years, Hitler's program of genocide of other races.

Abortion-on-demand was legalized in 1973 in all fifty of the United States by a ruling of the U.S. Supreme Court. Subsequently there appeared a sharply increased interest in, and varying degrees of increased pressure for, Definition of Death bills, legalization of living wills, so-called Death Dignity bills, and even direct euthanasia bills. Whether or not the legalization of the killing (by abortion) of humans who are unwanted or defective on the legal basis of age (too young) and place of residence (still living in the womb), does in fact establish an ethic, which if extended logically, will also some day justify legalizing the killing of other humans for the same reasons, (unwanted or defective) and on similar legal bases, of age (too old), and place of residence (certain institutions), remains to be seen. With almost no exceptions, pro-life leaders are firmly convinced of a direct relationship. Many, but not all, pro-abortion ("pro-choice") people just as directly deny any such relationship.

Whether such a progression, such a cause and effect, does exist is for the reader to judge and the passing of time to confirm. However, the full story of the only major euthanasia program that has occurred in modern times is certainly a profoundly important subject for study.

With the permission of the Macmillan Company and the full cooperation of Dr. Wertham, we are pleased to make available to you the story of the German Euthanasia Program as told in such fascinating detail in chapters 8 and 9 of his book, *A Sign for Cain.*

Hayes Publishing Company

Contents

I

"Looking at Potatoes from Below"

ADMINISTRATIVE MASS KILLINGS

> What kind of murder is it, which not only
> many suffer, but which also many com-
> mit?
> —DIETRICH GOLDSCHMIDT, Professor
> of Sociology, Berlin

THE administrative mass killings of the Nazi era constitute something new in the rich history of human violence. Even individuals
cannot be completely understood henceforth without a realization
of how easy it is for a civilized society to revert to a state of
brutality. No single deed or event of this period is entirely new.
But the total process is new. It manifests itself on different levels—
political, psychological, military, institutional, and economic. It is
a mixture of brutality, efficiency, and cynicism about human life.
From the concentration camp Flossenbürg in Bavaria, where
thousands of resistance fighters were killed, a guard wrote in a
letter to a friend that there was always room there for more people
"because from time to time some of them look at the potatoes
from below."

The methods by which the victims were killed, their numbers,
the deliberate inclusion of women and children, and the way it
was rationalized, accepted, defended, and perpetrated are all a
recent dimension of violence. We cannot visualize this from big
generalizations, but only from typical examples. In the neighbor-
hood of the Serbian town of Kragujevac, partisans clashed with
a Nazi detachment. As a result, 6,000 inhabitants of the town
were later seized as hostages and killed. Among them was a whole

secondary school, of which the director, the teacher, and every single pupil were killed. Such acts were not committed, as is sometimes stated, by "outsiders of society." They were carried out by ordinary people and planned, ordered, and acknowledged by the highest authorities.

The mass killing in concentration camps cannot be subsumed under any of the old categories. It is not bestial, because even the most predatory animals do not exterminate their own species. It is not barbaric, because barbarians did not have such organized, planned, and advanced techniques for killing people and processing them into such commercial products as fertilizers. It is not medieval —it is indeed very twentieth century. It is not strictly a national matter, for the perpetrators had no difficulty in finding collaborators —even very active ones—in other countries. It is not a past, historical episode, because it is still largely unresolved legally, politically, psychologically and educationally. It is not a unique occurrence, because there is no certainty whatsoever that it will not be repeated when similar circumstances arise. It is not an unforeseeable natural catastrophe, because it was long foreshadowed. It is not the work of madmen, for many of the perpetrators and organizers led (both before and after the killings) normal, average bourgeois, working-class, professional, aristocratic, or intellectual lives. The term "genocide" covers only a part of it (although a very large one), because the earliest part was strictly political: Germans killing Germans. It was not a disorderly orgy of primitive violence but a mass action lasting years and carried out with pedantic orderliness.

A mass murderer used to be a man who killed maybe four or five or, say, even ten or fifteen people. Those were what are called the good old days. Now mass killing involves hundreds or thousands. These numbers are so large that we can hardly imagine them. It is also difficult to apply to them the categories of individual responsibility, guilt, being an accessory, punishment, and so on.

The people killed in concentration camps included political prisoners, Jews (the largest number), gypsies (the most completely exterminated group), Slavs, prisoners of war, and undesirable civilians. It has been estimated that 7,500,000 people were confined in concentration camps, of whom a bare 500,000 survived, many with serious mental and physical aftereffects. The number of Jews killed in concentration camps and outside is estimated at between 5,000,000 and 6,000,000.

By 1945 there were in Germany, Austria, and occupied countries more than a thousand concentration camps. Among them were:

Auschwitz (Oswiecim)
Belsen, near Hanover
Belzec, in Poland, the first big concentration camp where gas chambers were installed; about 600,000 victims died there
Birkenau, the poetically named camp (meaning "meadow of white birches") which was part of the Auschwitz complex
Buchenwald, near Weimar
Chelmo (Kulmhof)
Dachau, one of the earliest central camps
Dora, in Thuringia, part of the Buchenwald complex, where V-2 rockets were manufactured by slave labor and many died in the subterranean installations
Flossenbürg, in Bavaria, for political prisoners and others
Gross-Rosen
Hellerberg, near Dresden; nearly all its inmates were later killed in Auschwitz
Hohnstein, in Saxony, which was regarded as one of the worst
Janowska, in Poland
Maidanek, also in Poland, one of the largest annihilation camps
Mauthausen, in Austria
Natzweiler, in Alsace
Neuengamme, near Hamburg
Oranienburg, near Berlin, one of the earliest camps
Ravensbrück, in Brandenburg, a central death camp for women, where 92,000 women and children were killed
Sachsenhausen
Sobibor, in Poland
Theresienstadt (Terezin), in Czechoslovakia
Treblinka, in Poland

From Belzec, Sobibor, and Treblinka, the authorities, after deduction of all overhead and expenses for transportation, derived pure profits of $44,500,000, profits which were handled by the Reichsbank and the Ministry of Economics. (This sum included profits from the victims' possessions, clothes, gold teeth, hair, and so on.)

We are apt to think of concentration camps as enclosures with a few buildings surrounded by barbed-wire fences and located in isolated places. In reality there were barracks, many buildings, big industrial installations, factories, railway stations with regular railway services, ramps, roads, connections with nearby towns and villages, big warehouses for products from the corpses and the victims' belongings, installations for torture and killing, research institutes, distribution centers, gas ovens, crematory furnaces, human-bone-milling plants, well-appointed kennels for hundreds of police dogs, agricultural fields, gardens for the officials, and so on. Some of the bigger camps were in reality groups or systems of different camps. All this in the aggregate covered large territories and involved wide communications. These ramifications alone show the absurdity of the claim and belief that the population knew nothing about them. These camps were going concerns. Thousands of people in the camps and in the population had working contacts with them.

The methods used in these camps were varied. They included, among others, shooting, hanging, poisoning, torturing, beating to death, "extermination by labor" (*i.e.,* working to death), starvation, carbolic acid injections into the heart, burning alive, wounding and leaving to die in mass graves with others already dead, vivisection, stomping, drowning, electrocution, locking as a group in a bunker and throwing hand grenades into it, freezing either in icy water or from standing naked in snow, clubbing or kicking to death, and keeping people packed in upright position in a cell with only standing room till they died.

One aspect of the administrative mass murders was the inclusion of children. This fact has been generally soft-pedaled and is little mentioned. This is an omission which helps to obscure the whole picture of the violence of our time. It has been estimated that about 1,500,000 children were killed, ranging in age from infancy up. Many of them were asphyxiated in gas ovens. The expression generally used for this procedure was "chasing the children up the chimney." The child phase of the mass murders had three features. First, it was carried out with the greatest brutality. Second, it was not a matter of individual excesses (although that happened often too, especially for sexual reasons), but was part of the routine and a regular constituent of policy and strategy mapped out at the desks of highly placed officials. Third, it was not carried out only by the SS; ordinary people did it as well. Painful medical experiments that often led to death were also carried out on children by physicians.

We can best imagine the official attitude toward children in concentration camps from a scene that took place in Auschwitz. A young child walked straight through the camp. Around his neck was hung on a string a placard with his name on it in big letters. That was most unusual. Why was he wearing it? He was the son of the camp leader, Aumeier, on his way to visit his father, and if he had not worn such a sign he might have been snatched up on the spot and tossed into one of the gas ovens.

There are two kinds of violence. The first is violence accompanied by emotion: feelings of hate, sadism, sex, and other passions. The second variety has very little to do with the personal passions of men. It is impersonal and bureaucratic, and those who order, commission, and organize it as well as those who execute it have extremely little feeling for their victims, be it sympathy or hate. They are executioners or slaughterers. Among the Nazi killings were many examples of sadistic cruelty, but the bulk of these killings was on a different plane. It is difficult to grasp intellectually or emotionally the reality of these assembly-line executions. We must string together a whole list of adjectives to convey their nature: collective, bureaucratic, administrative, methodical, planned, calculated, organized, systematic, stereotyped, routine, efficient, impersonal, purposeful. As one survivor expressed it, it was "a fantastically well-organized, spick-and-span hell."

The roots of this callousness go back to the time before the Nazi regime. The twenties in Central Europe was not only the time of the Weimar Republic of Thomas Mann and the Bauhaus, but also very much the time of the rise of extreme reactionary groups, who made no secret of their intentions. The portents of this previolence phase were not recognized then and are not even fully recognized historically now. If we do not follow all the sources of the administrative mass murders, it means that these victims have not only suffered, they have suffered in vain. Odd Nansen, the son of the explorer and Nobel Peace Prize winner Fridtjof Nansen, was an inmate of the Sachsenhausen concentration camp. He described his experiences and observations and wrote: "The worst crime you can commit today against yourself and society is to forget what happened and sink back into indifference. It was the indifference of mankind that let it take place."

We should not regard the Nazi mass killings of civilians in isolation. Many extensive massacres and exterminations have occurred in the past: the Crusades (a million victims); the Massacre of St. Bartholomew's Day; the Inquisition (a quarter of a million); the burning of witches (at least 20,000); the subjection of colonies in South America (more than 15,000,000); the island of Haiti (14,000 survivors out of 1,000,000 inhabitants after thirty-five years of colonization); the extermination of the Indians in Argentina and Uruguay, the island of Mauritius (the work slaves died so fast that 1,200 had to be imported annually); Java (the Dutch East India Company extorted in twelve years $830,000,000 from the slave labor of 5,000,000 natives, untold numbers of whom perished); the Congo (of 30,000,000 inhabitants at the time of its colonial take-over, 8,500,000 were still alive in 1911); India (open violence such the Amritsar Massacre: during the dispersal of an assemblage, 379 were killed and 1,500 wounded, in an episode which had a lasting effect on Nehru's political development); the Indians in the United States (the great anthropologist Henry Lewis Morgan had the courage to denounce their vilification); Nanking (the massacre by the Japanese); the Hereros in Southwest Africa (40,000 men, women, and children were surrounded, driven to the desert, and left to die of hunger and thirst. Neither the German Parliament nor the traders or missionaries protested. Report of the German General Staff: the Hereros had ceased "to exist as an independent tribe." The General Staff today is the same institution with the same traditions. General Heusinger, former chief of the General Staff and presently chairman of the NATO Permanent Military Committee in Washington, used the expression "merciless hardness"); Armenians (1,500,000 were driven from the place they had cultivated for more than 2,000 years; many men, women, and children were massacred or left to perish in the desert); and so on and on.

These massacres have a number of features in common. They are not usually committed by the hotheaded anonymous groups or mobs which we like to accuse, but by cold-blooded ruling powers, for material advantages. They are characterized by a mixture of commercial and sadistic motives, by cruelty, by the vilification of victims regarded as subpeople and not really human, by the failure —or connivance—of what one might regard as restraining agencies and institutions. The history books tell us little about these events, although much can be learned from them. Viewed against this background, the Nazi holocaust appears as the historical intersection of past vilifications and unresolved violences.

What makes the Nazi administrative mass killings so outstanding is not their numbers, their efficiency, or their cruelty, but the fact that they occurred in an epoch when nobody thought it was humanly or socially possible. Therein lies their deepest lesson. If it was possible then, why not again? What has fundamentally changed? The curtain may have gone down—but only for the intermission. No social scientist or psychologist had predicted that near the mid-century some 8,000,000 nonparticipants in any war action would be deliberately killed. Is it not indicated for behavioral scientists to reexamine their perspective and to realize how closely violence is interwoven in the very fabric of our social life?

A strong economic lever promoted the mass violence. The material interestedness involved the state, the big corporations, and countless ordinary people who profited. Until February, 1945, the police and SS bureaucrat Himmler met frequently with his advisory circle of thirty to forty leading industrialists, bankers, and other members of the economic elite. A high-level order from the central office of the SS addressed to the commanders of all concentration camps said: "It is self-understood that the first thing to be considered is the hundred percent economic use of the inmates."

The commercialization of mass violence proceeded along five main lines:

1. Slave labor

2. Disposal of victims' property and personal belongings
3. Commercial utilization of human bodies
4. Supplying gas chambers and crematory furnaces as well as chemicals, for killing and disposing of bodies
5. Using victims as test objects for commercial products

Slave Labor

Slave labor had a tremendous, still vastly underrated importance, both as a way of killing and as a method of making profits. It was a matter not only of lives but of ledgers as well. As a report to Himmler stated, the concentration camps had to be shaped from their "one-sided political form into an organization corresponding to the economic tasks." Protocols of conferences are extant in which Himmler and Goebbels agreed on the principle of "extermination by labor." The rationale of the procedure—and it *was* a rationale and not irrational sadism—was to give the inmates as little as possible to eat and to make them work until they died of exhaustion or (when they could not possibly work any more) to kill them. There was only a short step between exploitation and extermination. This treatment was to be applied on the largest scale to Jews, Russians, Poles, Czechs, gypsies, prisoners of war, German criminals and political prisoners. Lieutenant General Helmar Moser of the German Army, former military commander of the town of Lublin, expressed it to a court this way: "The doomed people in the camp were forced to perform extremely hard work beyond their strength and were urged on by brutal beatings." Or, as a Nazi official put it: "Those harnessed to the labor process work willingly on the basis of continuous fear of death." Among these slave laborers were many children under fifteen. They had to work under the same murderous conditions as the adults.

A common practice was to have weakened prisoners, "slow workers," exchanged for sturdier ones. The weak ones were disposed of. They were sent to a place with mass-killing equipment and were killed. This was part of the routine of the whole industrial procedure. A regular weekly report of I. G. Auschwitz (part of the dye trust I. G. Farben) for the period from February 8, 1943 on, states that the SS and the industry managers "agreed that all weak prisoners could be got rid of so that we have the guarantee of almost full working performance."

Slave labor was used in three main localities: in general concentration camps; in plants and factories organized and operated by private industrial firms near and in intimate collaboration with concentration camps; in plants away from the camps, like the I. G. Farben factory at Ludwigshafen. The revealing term "company camps" (*Firmenlager*) came into general usage.

Inmates had to work long hours—usually eleven hours—including Sundays and holidays. From 1933 to 1945 the expenses for the SS for one inmate averaged about ten cents a day. That included board, clothing, "supervision," housing. Inmates were rented out to private industry at the price of $1 a day or, for skilled workers, $1.50 a day. That made a huge profit for the SS, which, as is often overlooked, became a very big commercial undertaking itself and also piled up enormous profits for the private industrial corporations from the cheap labor.

Executives, engineers, and managers of the private industrial corporations knew, of course, of their labor supply, its source, the conditions of work, and the final fate of the exhausted laborers. Many of them inspected the scene. In Auschwitz they were shown the crematorium. Some complained of the "terrible smell" from the cremation furnaces. In camp Dora there was a special building with a large chimney which smoked almost constantly, where the bodies of the laborer-victims were cremated. Nobody who saw the inside of the camp could have missed this building and its purpose.

In one of the subcamps of the Buchenwald compound, which was operated directly by and for the big electrical company of Siemens, every six or eight weeks 500 inmates perished. But the camp's quota of 15,000 laborers was kept filled by replacements. According to the minutes of their meetings, the directors of the Siemens company over a period of several years discussed the progress of requisitioning this slave labor to replace the dead.

Even in private industrial plants employing slave labor, where there were no concentration-camp commanders and no SS, the firms assigned to themselves the right to work people to death and kill them with impunity. For example, the Leipzig concern Hasag maintained three plants in Poland. In all three there were barbed-wire-enclosed camps under the surveillance of the private civilian company guards. Inmates were tortured, bitten by dogs set on them, and even literally beaten to death. One of the plants had its own place of execution for laborers too starved or exhausted to work any more. Even pregnant women were executed there. The SS had nothing to do with this. It was private enterprise. Involved in this routine of mistreatment and murder, and tried in court after the war, were managers, masters, foremen, factory guards, and twenty-three directors of this private concern.

The revenue from slave labor was carefully computed. According to official documents, the average duration of a slave laborer's life was nine months. (In Auschwitz, according to testimony of SS physician Dr. Muench, it was six months.) Each item was carefully figured out: the daily income from renting out prisoners; from this was subtracted the cost of feeding them and the depreciation of their clothes; subtracted also were the costs of cremating them. Added to the gain was the rational utilization of the corpse: the gold from the teeth; the clothes in which they were arrested; their valuables and whatever money they may have had on them. Especially to be added were the proceeds from the commercial utilization of their bones and their ashes. Finally the total gain was calculated on an "average duration of life of nine months."

Some of the large industrial concerns had an insatiable demand for more and more cheap slave labor. The percentage of such labor in some industries was at times very great. For example, at one time fully one-half of the 200,000 workers employed by I. G. Farben were slave laborers. The branches of industry which employed this labor were very diverse: chemicals, rubber, armament, electrical equipment, china, granite and stone quarries, construction, mineral water, textiles, leather, building, and so on. Among the better-known names of firms employing this slave labor from concentration camps are Krupp, Siemens, AEG (General Electric Company), I. G. Farben, Volkswagen-Works, Messerschmitt, Junkers-Works, Heinkel, Argus-Works, Continental Rubber, Daimler-Benz, Shell (Floridsdorf, near Vienna), and Bavarian

Motor Works. Some commercial undertakings involved in slave labor are now closely connected with American capital, so that this period merges into our own economic system.

Disposal of Property and Personal Belongings

A further source of considerable income was that from the disposal and utilization of the property of the victims who perished. Apart from the property confiscated, such as furniture, furnishings, and similar items from domiciles, this consisted of personal belongings such as clothes, jewelry, cameras, and so on. This added up to a vast amount of material, which in the aggregate represented huge sums of money. There were shoes of every description, for men, women, and children (in Maidanek 820,000 pairs of footwear, from babies' shoes to soldiers' boots, were found); underwear; thousands of spectacles; men's ties; women's belts; robes; watches; mountains of children's toys; nipples for babies' feeding bottles; scissors; suitcases; artificial limbs; and so on. All these articles were collected, carefully sorted, packed, stacked, and dispatched to central places. The commercial and financial phases were negotiated and handled by the civil servants in the Reichsbank and the Ministry of Economics.

Utilization of Human Bodies

How human bodies were turned to profitable account forms a unique chapter in the history of violence. And it is not old history but contemporary history. Even in ancient times, what we call primitive people made graves for the dead; they did not utilize or barter parts of the bodies. That was left to the civilized barbarism of *our* time.

In the First World War, British Intelligence spread a false story that the Germans were making soap from corpses. It was left to the Second World War to make this a reality.

In Gdansk (Danzig) during the Second World War, a brick building was erected for a factory for a new branch of industry. Here methods were worked out for the utilization of human fat to make soap and human skin to make boots, briefcases, and bags. In the basement of the building there were large square concrete baths covered with zinc sheeting. Ten bodies were placed in carbolic acid solutions in each bath. Experts have established that among those who were shot, hanged or clubbed before being so treated, some still showed signs of life. In one room of the factory were big boilers in which the human soap was made. This was successful, and specimens of the soap (in pails) are still extant. The production of human leather did not progress so far and led only to semifinished articles of tanned human skin.

This industry was designed and organized by scientists and doctors. Even courses for production of human soap were given to other doctors from different concentration camps. Of course, such an industry was feasible only on the basis of a policy of mass extermination. The existence of this undertaking for the use of human raw material for soap factories and tanneries was no secret. Prominent people visited the place, including the rector of Danzig University, the Minister of Health, the Minister of National Education.

Gold teeth and fillings were taken out of the mouths of those who died or were killed in the concentration camps. No corpse could be burned without a stamp on the chest: "Inspected for gold fillings." This added up to thousands of pounds of gold.

Women's hair, and men's as well, was cut off, collected, and stored in sacks or barrels. Then it was sold, to be used for the production of felt hats, mattresses, and other felt products. A private felt factory in Roth near Nuremberg did a flourishing business of this kind.

The ashes of those cremated were utilized as fertilizer. That made a lot of fertilizer and represented a great economic asset. It was used on fields and in gardens. There were also special mills for the grinding of human bones. A very efficient mass-production bone-milling plant existed, for example, in the camp Chelmo, near Posen. Both ground bones and ashes were placed in large tin cans and shipped all over Germany for fertilizing the fields. Even a special method for using small human bones and ashes as fertilizer was worked out. It consisted of "a layer of human bones, a layer of human ashes, a layer of manure."

Supplying Machinery for Extermination

The supplying of crematories, gas furnaces, and chemicals for killing and disposing of bodies became a lucrative business for large private concerns. No businessman seems to have had the slightest scruples about it. And with the introduction of gas ovens and big crematory furnaces, mass murder became industrialized. This is something new in the history of both violence and economics. Perfectly legitimate and highly regarded concerns took part in it. For example, a big electrical company, Siemens, devised and manufactured gas-chamber installations in which the murders were carried out. The company had a monopoly on gas-chamber electrical equipment. It introduced new and ingenious devices. Among them was a ventilating system by which gas could be drawn out and fresh gas blown in quickly. This made it possible to kill as many as 10,000 persons within a twenty-four-hour period.

Chemicals and poison gas, like Zyklon B gas (which gives off cyanide when exposed to the air), were manufactured for the purpose of mass killing in the camps by the big chemical concern I. G. Farben (the subsidiary firm Degesch). With these products, wholesale numbers of prisoners, including the spent slave laborers who worked in their own plants, were exterminated. In other words, you earn money by obtaining cheap prison laborers, and then you make more money by selling the means to kill them when they get exhausted.

Mass killing presented new technical problems. What to do with the corpses for instance? At first that seemed an unsolvable question. But it was solved by using the most modern equipment for burning garbage and refuse in a large city and transforming the bodies into usable products. In the city of Berlin it had been found that high temperatures—up to 1,400 degrees Centigrade— were needed to accomplish this. Exactly the same method was introduced in the concentration-camp crematory furnaces. In Maidanek, for example, temperatures of 1,500 degrees Centigrade were used. The crematorium there, a huge stone building with a big factory chimney, was the world's largest.

Use of Prisoners as Test Objects for Commercial Products

Another economic gain from mass violence was the use of human beings as test objects for experiments with marketable pharmaceutical products and with chemical war weapons such as poison gas. A letter from an official of the I. G. Farben chemical trust to the Auschwitz concentration-camp administration is typical of the matter-of-fact use of human guinea pigs: "We have received the 150 women we asked for. Although extremely exhausted, they met our requirements. The tests were successful. All the subjects died. We are soon starting negotiations for another lot." Children were used in the same way. For example, six girl inmates aged eight to fourteen were infected with hepatitis to try out a new remedy for this disease. The name Murder, Inc., would have been more appropriate for the firms which supplied the installations and chemicals for the specific purpose of mass killing of civilians and disposal of their bodies than for the gangster syndicate which was responsible for a mere thousand murders.

Some of the cruel medical experiments on inmates to test new drugs did not originate in the heads of individual doctors, but were asked for and initiated by pharmaceutical firms. This combination of business, pharmacology, and violence is a significant sociological fact. There is, for example, the scene of the group of prisoners in the Sachsenhausen concentration camp marching—singing and whistling—under the influence of a new energy pill that was being tested for a pharmaceutical firm. They were marching like this to their death in the gas chamber.

These inhuman experiments are not a thing of the past. They are still taken for granted and commercially cited. One of the cruelest and most painful medical experiments in the Dachau camp was the immersion of inmates in ice-cold water. Some were given a drug; those in a control group were not. It was claimed that those who got the drug survived, while those who did not died. Now, two decades later, advertising specifically refers to these "cold water experiments" in promoting this same drug (which is, incidentally, of very doubtful value).

The cheap labor furnished by concentration-camp inmates was an enormous economic asset. We cannot do justice to these cruel facts psychoanalytically alone. Slave labor did not satisfy any deep aggressive instincts; it satisfied the stockholders. The historian J. Schmelzer, of the Martin Luther University in Halle-Wittenberg, made an interesting sociological study of the responsible officials of the I. G. Farben concern who were involved in the slave-labor period and what positions they hold today. The study shows how the action phase of this mass violence merges imperceptibly into the respectability of the postviolence phase. An interesting sidelight is the fact that Friedrich Vialon, a high Nazi official who had to do with the renting out of slave laborers to private industry, is today State Secretary in the ministry for aid to underdeveloped countries.

What happened to the firms who used slave labor? Many of them, or their successors, are doing fine. Their shares are sound financially, even if not morally. Some of the prominent men and concerns involved in these sources of labor today hold more concentrated economic power than ever. This means that in the postviolence phase, violence was not resolved but was rewarded.

The Krupp concern built places of production near such death camps as Auschwitz. In the places of production, thousands of inmates were worked half—or rather three-quarters—to death, then in the camps they were pushed the rest of the way. The number of Krupp forced laborers in the original factories and the camp plants comprised at least 75,000 civilians and 25,000 prisoners of war. Alfred Krupp, head of the firm, was sentenced to twelve years in jail for the use and abuse of slave labor. Long before his sentence was due to expire, after four years in a pleasant prison, he went free. His release was celebrated in the biggest hotel in town with a champagne breakfast. He gave a press conference for more than fifty press representatives at a flower-decorated table and was greeted like a national hero. Asked whether he would repent what he had done, he replied that he had not thought out philosophically the ramifications of his conduct. Judging by what has happened since, we have not either. Today, with an assist from the financial and political establishment of the United States, he is head of one of the largest individually owned industrial concerns in the world. In 1957 there was a great celebration of his fiftieth birthday. As of 1965 the Krupp group had net assets of more than a billion dollars and was entirely owned by Alfred Krupp. The company now produces twice as much steel as it did before World War II.

This is a twentieth-century success story—success for the perpetration of violence. For since the violence of slave labor worked so well, financially speaking, it is an endorsement and a direct incentive for the future. In a wider perspective the firms which profit from the apartheid conditions in South Africa play a role comparable to that of the industries in Germany which profited from slave labor directly. In a typical year (1962), American companies operating in South Africa made profits of $72,000,000. That is double the average revenue from American investments abroad (11.8 percent).

What was in the minds of those who participated in one way or another in the administrative mass murders? According to the federal bureau charged with the prosecution of Nazi crimes, 80,000 persons participated in the exterminations. Of course, some of them were abnormal, sadistic, hostility-ridden personalities who acted from uncontrolled primitive drives. But in view of the very large numbers of participants in these massacres, the problem of individual character recedes into the background. Only social psychology can help us to understand this collective behavior. Many of these persons not only were inhuman officials but were officially inhuman. At the one pole were those who carried out the deeds; at the other, those who may be called the desk murderers, the intellectual originators. In between were the middlemen of murder. In vain do we look for any number of colorful, eccentric personalities. Instead we find a large gray mass of functionaries, bureaucrats, and rank-and-file killers. Here were the policy makers, the diplomats who made the orders palatable for foreign consumption, men who gave the orders, the transmitters of the orders, the organizers and supervisors, the civil servants, the technical personnel, the legal experts, the physicians (present in every concentration camp and acting like anything but physicians), the clerks, the workers, the approving bystanders and spectators.

It has frequently been stated that the population as a whole just accepted the political directives and responded passively. Sociological analysis of the evidence from the first years of the regime, when the mass violence started, indicates that this is not true. The people did not take the avalanche of authoritarian violence without question. We can reconstruct a whole fever curve: puzzlement, indecisiveness, refusal, illusion, awakening, awareness of the closing in of the propaganda and the violence, insecurity, passive resistance, disappointment with the wrong prognostications of the liberal leaders, emptiness, anxiety, hope of help from other countries, helplessness, resignation, toleration, disappointment, indifference, submission, fascination with the new dynamic regime, adherence. During this period while the victims lost their freedom, many intellectuals lost their convictions.

The central fact that stands out from the study of the administrative mass murders is the power of incitement. It can corrode the thinking of the innocent. People, practically all people, can be incited to violence. They may not all carry it out themselves; they may only help from a distance and tolerate and thereby foster it. But it is a fallacy to assume that the majority of right-thinking people are immune to these mass influences and that only predisposed personalities succumb to them. Even the good man, as George Gissing wrote long ago, "becomes ready for any evil to which contagion prompts him." If we place all our emphasis on the unconscious, we neglect the role of conscious manipulation.

Effective incitement to violence does not proceed as simple, direct suggestion or exhortation. It always has to be combined, as Georges Sorel, a political theoretician of violence, has pointed out, with a "myth." One such suitable myth consists in the complete vilification of opponents. They are the ones toward whom heroic hardness is to be shown. Along with the myth that the life of other people has no value goes a tremendous, pleasant feeling of superiority. An SS man put it this way in his diary: "How superior we feel after each one of the Fuehrer's speeches!" If the potential opponents are regarded as subhuman, as subpeople, their complete destruction becomes morally permissible and even necessary. We underestimate the absolute cruelty that can be engendered in this way and only in this way.

The next step follows with a certain inevitability. For both the higher ranks—the planners—and the lower ranks—the doers—it became a habit to use violence for settling tasks and solving problems. This habit became more and more ingrained. When Abe Reles, one of the executioners of Murder, Inc., was asked by the District Attorney, "Did your conscience ever bother you?" he answered, "How did you feel when you tried your first law case?" The District Attorney replied that he was nervous but that later he got used to it. And Reles responded, "It's the same with murder. I got used to it."

II

The Geranium in the Window

THE "EUTHANASIA" MURDERS

> If the physician presumes to take into
> consideration in his work whether a life
> has value or not, the consequences are
> boundless and the physician becomes the
> most dangerous man in the state.
> —DR. CHRISTOPH HUFELAND
> (1762–1836)

IF we want to understand violence as a whole, we cannot leave any
of its major manifestations in a fog of half-knowledge. But this
is exactly what has happened with an unprecedented occurrence
of mass violence, the deliberate killing of large numbers of mental
patients, for which psychiatrists were directly responsible. To
both the general public and the psychiatric profession, the details
and the background are still imperfectly known. This is not only
a chapter in the history of violence; it is also a chapter in the
history of psychiatry. Silence does not wipe it out, minimizing
it does not expunge it. It must be faced. We must try to understand
and resolve it.

It should be kept in mind at the outset that it is a great achieve-
ment of psychiatry to have brought about the scientific and humane
treatment of mental patients after centuries of struggles against
great obstacles. In this progress, as is universally acknowledged,
German psychiatrists played a prominent part. And German public
psychiatric hospitals had been among the best and most humane
in the world.

In the latter part of 1939, four men, in the presence of a whole
group of physicians and an expert chemist, were purposely killed
(with carbon monoxide gas). They had done nothing wrong, had
caused no disturbance, and were trusting and cooperative. They

25

were ordinary mental patients of a state psychiatric hospital which was—or should have been—responsible for their welfare. This successful experiment led to the installation of gas chambers in a number of psychiatric hospitals (Grafeneck, Brandenburg, Hartheim, Sonnenstein, Hadamar, Bernburg).

Let us visualize a historical scene. Dr. Max de Crinis is professor of psychiatry at Berlin University and director of the psychiatric department of the Charité, one of the most famous hospitals of Europe. He is one of the top scientists and organizers of the mass destruction of mental patients. Dr. de Crinis visits the psychiatric institution Sonnenstein, near Dresden, to supervise the working of his organization. He wants to see how the plans are carried out. Sonnenstein is a state hospital with an old tradition of scientific psychiatry and humaneness. In the company of psychiatrists of the institution, Dr. de Crinis now inspects the latest installation, a shower-roomlike chamber. Through a small peephole in an adjoining room he watches twenty nude men being led into the chamber and the door closed. They are not disturbed patients, just quiet and cooperative ones. Carbon monoxide is released into the chamber. The men get weaker and weaker; they try frantically to breathe, totter, and finally drop down. Minutes later their suffering is over and they are all dead. This is a scene repeated many, many times throughout the program. A psychiatrist or staff physician turns on the gas, waits briefly, and then looks over the dead patients afterward, men, women, and children.

The mass killing of mental patients was a large project. It was organized as well as any modern community psychiatric project, and better than most. It began with a careful preparatory and planning stage. Then came the detailed working out of methods, the formation of agencies for transporting patients, their registration and similar tasks (there were three main agencies with impressive bureaucratic names), the installing of crematory furnaces at the psychiatric institutions, and finally the action. It all went like clockwork, the clock being the hourglass of death. The organization comprised a whole chain of mental hospitals and institutions, university professors of psychiatry, and directors and staff members of mental hospitals. Psychiatrists completely reversed their historical role and passed death sentences. It became a matter of routine. These psychiatrists, without coercion, acted not figuratively but literally in line with the slogan of one of the most notorious concentration-camp commanders, Koch, the husband of Ilse Koch: "There are no sick men in my camp. They are either well or dead."

The whole undertaking went by different designations: "help for the dying," "mercy deaths," "mercy killings," "destruction of life devoid of value," "mercy action"—or, more briefly, the "action." They all became fused in the sonorous and misleading term "euthanasia." Strangely enough—or perhaps not so strangely —the name has persisted. We hear and read of the "euthanasia program," "euthanasia experiments," "euthanasia campaign," "euthanasia action," "euthanasia trials." In reality, these mass killings had nothing whatever to do with euthanasia. These were not mercy deaths but merciless murders. It was the merciless destruction of helpless people by those who were supposed to help them. There was nothing individual about it; it was a systematic, planned, massive killing operation. The whole proceeding was characterized by the complete absence of any compassion, mercy, or pity for the individual. What a physician does or should do with a special individual patient under special circumstances had absolutely nothing to do with those mass exterminations.

The greatest mistake we can make is to assume or believe that there was a morally, medically, or socially legitimate program and that all that was wrong was merely the excesses. There were no excesses. Rarely has a civil social action been planned, organized, and carried through with such precision. It was not a "good" death, as the term "euthanasia" implies (from *eu,* "well," and *thanatos,* "death"), but a bad death; not a euthanasia but what may be called a dysthanasia. Often it took up to five minutes of suffocation and suffering before the patients died. If we minimize the cruelty involved (or believe those who minimize it), these patients are betrayed a second time. It was often a slow, terrible death for them. For example, a male nurse of one of the state mental hospitals described the routine he saw through the peephole of the gas chamber: "One after the other the patients sagged and finally fell all over each other." Others have reported that the dead gassed victims were found with their lips pushed outward, the tip of the tongue stuck out between them, clearly showing that they had been gasping for breath.

The false term "euthanasia" was used by those who planned, organized, and carried out the action, and it is still being used now by those who do not know, or do not want to know, what really happened.

The ancients meant by euthanasia the art and discipline of dying in peace and dignity. The only legitimate medicosocial extension of this meaning is *help* toward that end, with special emphasis on relief from pain and suffering. Euthanasia in this sense is the mitigation and relief of pain and suffering of the death agony by medication or other medical means. For the physician, that means a careful diagnosis, prognosis, and consequent action in relation to a special clinical state. As in any other medical procedures, this may involve a certain risk which requires the physician's best responsible judgment in the individual case. Whatever problems this may represent, they have no relation whatsoever to this massacre of mental patients. To confuse the two means to confuse humanity with inhumanity.

When Dr. Hans Hoff, professor of psychiatry at the University of Vienna, begins his introduction to the recent book *Euthanasia and Destruction of Life Devoid of Value* like this: "As long as there are incurable, suffering and painfully dying people, the problem of euthanasia will be open to discussion," he is adding to the confusion and concealment, as does the author of this whitewashing book. These victims were not dying, they were not in pain, they were not suffering, and most of them were not incurable.

From the very beginning—that is, before the outbreak of war and before any written expression by Hitler—it was officially known to leading professors of psychiatry and directors of mental hospitals that under the designation of "euthanasia" a program was about to be carried through by them and with their help to kill mental patients in the whole of Germany. The object was "the destruction of life devoid of value." That definition was flexible enough for a summary proceeding of extermination of patients.

The term "euthanasia" was deliberately used to conceal the actual purpose of the project. But there is also a real confusion about the term that reaches into many quarters. In the *American*

College Dictionary, for example, "euthanasia" is defined as "the putting of a person to death painlessly." That is not euthanasia; it is homicide. If you "put a person to death," that is, deliberately kill him, you are committing murder. If it is done painlessly, it is still murder. Many murders, just like suicides, are committed without inflicting pain. In similar fashion, a widely used recent dictionary of psychological and psychoanalytical terms defines "euthanasia" as "the practice of ending life painlessly." Criminology is familiar with cases of mass murderers who made it a practice to do just that. For example, the man who over a considerable period of time lured good-looking young boys into the woods and put them to sleep, a sleep from which they never woke up. They were found, partly undressed, with peaceful expressions on their faces. That was not euthanasia, however; it was mass murder. The fact that such confused and confusing definitions are given in standard dictionaries is another documentation of my thesis that violence is much more solidly and insidiously set in our social thinking than is generally believed.

Just as the designation has been left in ambiguity, so also has the number of the victims. We read about "thousands" or "tens of thousands" or "almost a hundred thousand." But how many were there? One would think that this fact would be indispensable for understanding not only the history of violence but even that of psychiatry and of modern civilization in general. Yet in none of the publications, books, or news reports of recent years is a more-or-less-correct figure given. It is characteristic that without exception all the figures that are mentioned are far below the reality. The individual psychiatric hospitals were not so squeamish about the number of patients put to death while the program lasted. For example, in 1941 the psychiatric institution Hadamar celebrated the cremation of the ten thousandth mental patient in a special ceremony. Psychiatrists, nurses, attendants, and secretaries all participated. Everybody received a bottle of beer for the occasion.

We can get an idea of the proportional numbers involved by studying some partial but exact statistics referring to a special locality. From 1939 to 1945 the number of patients in the psychiatric hospitals of Berlin dropped to one-fourth of the original total. As the cause of this drop the official statistics give "evacuations." That is a euphemistic expression for the fact that three-fourths of the patients were transported to other institutions and killed. Sometimes patients slated for murder were not sent directly to the hospitals that had the proper installations, but went first temporarily to so-called intermediate institutions. In 1938 the psychiatric institutions of the province of Brandenburg had 16,295 mental patients of the city of Berlin. In 1945 only 2,379 were left. Almost 14,000 were destroyed. In the institution Berlin-Buch, of 2,500 patients, 500 survived; in the hospital of Kaufbeuren in Bavaria, of 2,000 patients, 200 were left. Many institutions, even big ones, *i.e.,* in Berlin, in Silesia, in Baden, in Saxony, in Austria, were closed entirely because all the patients had been liquidated.

In the special killing institutions the turnover was fast. The psychiatric institution Grafeneck normally had 100 beds. Early in the "action," within thirty-three days 594 patients died (*i.e.,* were killed). A while later, within forty-seven days 2,019 inmates were written off. Eventually the crematorium of Grafeneck smoked incessantly.

In 1939 about 300,000 mental patients (according to some figures it was 320,000) were in psychiatric hospitals, institutions, or clinics. In 1946 their number was 40,000. It was discussed during the project that 300,000 hospital beds would be made available by getting rid of mental patients.

The most reliable estimates of the number of psychiatric patients killed are at least 275,000. We have to realize particularly that the largest proportion of them were not "incurable," as is often lightly stated. Even if "euthanasia" is defined, as it falsely is, as "the killing of incurable mentally diseased persons," that is not at all what happened. According to the best established psychiatric knowledge, about 50 percent of them either would have improved to such an extent that they could have been discharged and lived a social life outside a hospital or would have gotten completely well.

Another misconception widely credited is that these patients had hereditary diseases. Even publications completely condemning the "euthanasia" action fall into this error. However, in the largest number of patients the hereditary factor played either no role at all or only the slightest (and that not well established scientifically). The whole number comprises both curable and incurable condi-

tions, psychopathic personalities, epileptics, encephalitics, neuro-
logical cases, mental defectives of both severe and mild degree,
arteriosclerotics, deaf-mutes, patients with all kinds of nervous
diseases, handicapped patients who had lost a limb in the First
World War and were in a state hospital, "cripples" of every description, *et al.*

The indications became wider and wider and eventually included as criteria "superfluous people," the unfit, the unproductive,
any "useless eaters," misfits, undesirables. The over-all picture is
best understood as the identification and elimination of the weak.

A considerable percentage of the whole number were senile
cases, including people who had no senile psychosis but were
merely aged and infirm. Many of the old people included in the
program were not in institutions but were living at home, in good
health, with their families. A psychiatrist would go to these homes
and give the aged people a cursory psychiatric examination. Of
course, it is easy, if you confront a very old person with a lot of
psychological questions, to make it appear that something is mentally wrong with him. The psychiatrist would then suggest that
such people be placed under guardianship and sent to an institution for a while. From there they were quickly put into gas chambers. It is difficult to conceive that thousands of normal men and
women would permit their parents or grandparents to be disposed
of in this way without more protest, but that is what happened.
As early as September, 1939, word had gotten about among the
population in Berlin that inmates of homes for the aged had been
exterminated and that it was planned to kill all aged invalids as
quickly as possible.

During the first phase of the program, Jewish mental patients,
old and young, were strictly spared and excluded. The reason given
was that they did not deserve the "benefit" of psychiatric euthanasia. This lasted up to the second half of 1940. Eventually they
were all rounded up, however, and by 1941, practically without
exception, were exterminated.

Thousands of children were disposed of. A special agency existed for them, consisting of a commission of three experts: one a
psychiatrist and director of a state hospital, the other two prominent pediatricians. The children came from psychiatric hospitals,

institutions for mental defectives, children's homes, university pediatric clinics, children's hospitals, pediatricians, *et al.* They were
killed in both psychiatric institutions and pediatric clinics. Especially in the latter a number of woman physicians were actively
involved in the murders. Among these children were those with
mental diseases, mental defectives—even those with only slightly
retarded intelligence—handicapped children, children with neuro-
logical conditions, and mongoloid children (even with minimal
mental defects). Also in this number were children in training
schools or reformatories. Admission to such child-care institutions
occurs often on a social indication and not for any intrinsic personality difficulties of the child. One physician who killed such
training-school boys and girls with intravenous injections of
morphia stated in court to explain his actions: "I see today that it
was not right. . . . I was always told that the responsibility lies
with the professors from Berlin."

The chief of the mental institution Hadamar was responsible for
the murder of "over a thousand patients." He personally opened
the containers of gas and watched through the peephole the death
agonies of the patients, including children. He stated: "I was of
course torn this way and that. It reassured me to learn what eminent scientists partook in the action: Professor Carl Schneider, Professor Heyde, Professor Nitsche." This, of course, is not an excuse
either legally or morally, but it is a causal factor which has to be
taken into account. And when Dr. Karl Brandt, the medical chief
of the euthanasia project, defended himself for his leading role in
the action, he stated that he had asked for the "most critical"
evaluation of who was mentally incurable. And he added: "Were
not the regular professors of the universities with the program?
Who could there be who was better qualified than they?"

These statements that leading psychiatrists supplied the rationalization for these cruelties and took a responsible part in them
are true. We must ask ourselves what was the prehistory, in the
previolence phase, of their ideas. Historically there were tendencies in psychiatry (and not only in German psychiatry) to pro-
nounce value judgments not only on individuals, on medical
grounds, but on whole groups, on medicosociological grounds.
What was (and still is) widely regarded as scientific writing pre-

pared the way. Most influential was the book *The Release of the Destruction of Life Devoid of Value,* published in Leipzig in 1920. Its popularity is attested by the fact that two years later a second edition became necessary. The book advocated that the killing of "worthless people" be released from penalty and legally permitted. It was written by two prominent scientists, the jurist Karl Binding and the psychiatrist Alfred Hoche. The concept of "life devoid of value" or "life not worth living" was not a Nazi invention, as is often thought. It derives from this book.

Binding and Hoche speak of "absolutely worthless human beings"; they plead for "the killing of those who cannot be rescued and whose death is urgently necessary"; they refer to those who are below the level of beasts and who have "neither the will to live nor to die"; they write about those who are "mentally completely dead" and who "represent a foreign body in human society." It is noteworthy that among the arguments adduced for killing, the economic factor is stressed, namely, the cost of keeping these patients alive and caring for them. The psychiatrist author decries any show of sympathy in such cases, because it would be based on "erroneous thinking." The jurist author recognizes that errors in diagnosis and execution might be made. But he dismisses that like this: "Humanity loses so many members through error that one more or less really hardly makes any difference." In the beginning of the book we read about the feeling of "pity" for the patient. But in the bulk of the text the question of pity does not come up any more. It gets completely lost. Instead, both authors enlarge on the economic factor, the waste of money and labor in the care of the retarded. Both extol "heroism" and a "heroic attitude" which our time is supposed to have lost.

These ideas were expressed in 1920. Surely Hoche and Binding had not heard of Hitler at that time, nor did Hitler read this book. It is not without significance that at this time, when Hitler was just starting his career, the "life devoid of value" slogan was launched from a different source. Evidently there is such a thing as a spirit of the times which emanates from the depths of economic-historical processes.

This little book influenced—or at any rate crystallized—the thinking of a whole generation. Considering how violence-stimulating the ideas in it are, it is significant that both authors were eminent men who played a role as intellectual leaders in a special historical period. This illustrates the proposition that violence does not usually come from the uncontrolled instincts of the under-educated, but frequently is a rationalized policy from above. Hoche was professor of psychiatry and director of the psychiatric clinic at Freiburg from 1902 to 1934. He made valuable contributions to neuropsychiatry. In his clinic a number of eminent specialists were trained—for example, Dr. Robert Wartenberg, who later became one of the outstanding and most popular teachers of neurology in California. Hoche's sound views on classification of mental diseases had considerable influence on American psychiatry, especially through Adolf Meyer, professor of psychiatry at Johns Hopkins.

Wherever his work touched on the social field, however, he had illiberal tendencies. For example, in a series of monographs which he edited, he published and gave wide currency to a book which tried to prove women intellectually inferior to men. In his work on forensic psychiatry, he exhibited a punitive, legalistic attitude with regard to sexual deviations. He was a reactionary opponent of psychoanalysis, not recognizing even Freud's well-established clinical observations. He regarded his book on the destruction of "life devoid of value" as one of his "more important" works.

The other author, Karl Binding, was professor of jurisprudence at the University of Leipzig. He was the chief representative of the retribution theory in criminal law. He combatted the idea that the protection of society is the purpose of punishment and that the personality of the criminal has to be taken into account. He taught that for every criminal deed there has to be full retribution. His son Rudolf G. Binding was also a jurist, and a recognized poet as well. When Romain Rolland in 1933 warned against Nazi violence and pleaded for humaneness, Rudolf G. Binding answered in a "Letter to the World." He advocated fanaticism on the part of everybody and called for "fanatics big and small, down to the children."

Another intellectual stream that contributed to the final massacre of mental patients was the exaggeration of the influence of heredity on mental disorders. The chief representative of this trend was Ernst Ruedin. Ruedin was professor of psychiatry at the universities of Basel, in Switzerland, and Munich. Some of his studies on heredity, and those of his pupils and associates (like Eugen Kahn, who later became professor of psychiatry at Yale), were undoubtedly valuable. This was widely recognized. He participated in the First International Congress for Mental Hygiene in Washington, D.C. But it was he who supplied the "scientific" reasons according to which mass sterilizations of all kinds of physically and mentally handicapped people took place. He was the chief architect of the compulsory sterilization law of 1933. This law was so vigorously formulated and interpreted (by Ruedin in 1934) that, for example, any young man with a harmless phimosis was forced to be sterilized. The summary official explanation for this was that he would be "incapable of achieving extraordinary performances in sport, in life, in war, or in overcoming dangers." The results of enforced castrations in the period from 1933 to 1945 are still quoted in current psychiatric literature without any critique of their inhumanity.

The compulsory sterilization law was the forerunner of the mass killing of psychiatric patients, which was organized and carried out with Ruedin's full knowledge. He expressly warned psychiatrists against the "excessive compassion and love of one's neighbor characteristic of the past centuries."

Against this theoretical-intellectual background, mental patients were sacrificed in psychiatric institutions and in the name of psychiatry. From its very inception the "euthanasia" program was guided in all important matters, including concrete details, by psychiatrists. The administrative sector was handled by bureaucrats who dealt merely with executive, management, and formal questions such as transport of patients, cremation, notification of relatives, and so on. Even the false death certificates were signed by psychiatrists. The psychiatrists made the decisions. For these physicians, as the physical chemist Professor Robert Havemann expressed it, denouncing the "euthanasia" murders, "the patient is no longer a human being needing help, but merely an object whose value is measured according to whether his life or his destruction is more expedient for the nation. The physicians took over the function of judge over life and death. . . . They made themselves into infallible gods." How matter-of-factly they considered this role is illustrated by the replies of the veteran director of one of the biggest and formerly most well-administered psychiatric hospitals during an interrogation:

Q. To how many children have you applied euthanasia in your hospital?
A. I couldn't tell you exactly. . . .
Q. To how many have you done that? 200? 500? 1,000?
A. For God's sake, I really don't remember how many there were. I really don't know whether there were a hundred or more.
Q. Do you know when euthanasia was practiced on the last child in your hospital?
A. I don't know exactly. But Dr. ——— says that until a short time before the arrival of the Americans [the American Army], children were still subjected to euthanasia.
Q. For how long have you practiced the euthanasia of children?
A. After so much time, I can't remember the dates exactly.
Q. When did the extermination of these children stop?
A. The extermination of these children never stopped until the end. I never received an order [to stop it].
Q. To how many adults did you apply euthanasia in your institution?
A. I don't know any more.
Q. How many adults have you submitted to euthanasia in your institution?
A. That didn't happen in my institution. I contented myself with transferring the patients [to other institutions where they were killed].

It has been stated that the psychiatrists were merely following a law or were being forced to obey an order. Again and again we read—as if it were a historical fact—of Hitler's secret order to exterminate those suffering from severe mental defect or disease. Those who hold the one-man theory of history (sometimes called the great-man theory of history), according to which important developments, for good or evil, are to be explained by the wish and will of one individual person, favor the illusion that such an order was the entire cause of the extermination of psychiatric patients. According to this view, everything was fine until that order was given and became fine again when the order was revoked. The reality was very different. There was no law and no such order. The tragedy is that the psychiatrists did not have to have an order.

They acted on their own. They were not carrying out a death sentence pronounced by somebody else. They were the legislators who laid down the rules for deciding who was to die; they were the administrators who worked out the procedures, provided the patients and places, and decided the methods of killing; they pronounced a sentence of life or death in every individual case; they were the executioners who carried the sentences out or—without being coerced to do so—surrendered their patients to be killed in other institutions; they supervised and often watched the slow deaths.

The evidence is very clear on this. The psychiatrists did not have to work in these hospitals; they did so voluntarily, were able to resign if they wished, and could refuse to do special tasks. For example, the psychiatrist Dr. F. Hoelzel was asked by the psychiatric director of the mental institution Eglfing-Haar to head a children's division in which many handicapped and disturbed children were killed (right up to 1945). He refused in a pathetic letter saying that his "temperament was not suited to this task," that he was "too soft."

Hitler gave no order to kill mental patients indiscriminately. As late as mid-1940 (when thousands of patients had been killed in psychiatric institutions), Minister of Justice Guertner wrote to Minister Hans Lammers: "The Fuehrer has declined to enact a law [for putting mental patients to death]." There was no legal sanction for it. All we have is one note, not on official stationery but on Hitler's own private paper, written in October, 1939, and predated September 1, 1939. Meetings of psychiatrists working out the "euthanasia" program had taken place long before that. Hitler's note is addressed to Philipp Bouhler, chief of Hitler's chancellery, and to Dr. Karl Brandt, Hitler's personal physician at the time and Reich Commissioner for Health. (Bouhler committed suicide; Dr. Brandt was sentenced to death and executed.) The note reads as follows:

Reichleader Bouhler and
Dr. Med. Brandt

are responsibly commissioned to extend the authority of physicians, to be designated by name, so that a mercy

death may be granted to patients who according to human judgment are incurably ill according to the most critical evaluation of
the state of their disease.

(Signed) Adolf Hitler

To kill patients (Hitler does not speak of mental patients), even
if one were sure that they are incurable, is bad enough. But even
if his wish, as the note clearly expresses it, had been executed, the
number of victims would have been infinitely smaller and the whole
proceeding could not have been carried out in the way in which it
was carried out. Referring to this note, anyone could have refused
to do what was later actually done. The note does not give the
order to kill, but the *power* to kill. That is something very different. The physicians made use of this power extensively, ruthlessly, cruelly. The note is not a command but an assignment of
authority and responsibility to a particular group of persons,
namely, physicians, psychiatrists, and pediatricians. This assignment, far from ordering it, did not even give psychiatrists official
permission to do what they did on a grand scale, *i.e.,* kill all kinds
of people who were not at all incurable or even mentally ill, making no attempt even to examine them first. The assignment gives
to the psychiatrist the widest leeway for "human judgment" and a
"most critical evaluation." It certainly cannot be construed as an
order to kill people with no serious disease or with no disease at all.

Even if the note was not meant to be taken literally, it was a
formal concession to ethics and offered a loophole for contradiction or at least question. The psychiatrists in authority did not take
advantage of this. Instead they initiated the most extreme measures
and cloaked them in scientific terminology and academic respectability. No mental patients were killed without psychiatrists being
involved. Without the scientific rationalization which they supplied
from the very beginning and without their mobilization of their
own psychiatric hospitals and facilities, the whole proceeding could
not have taken the shape it did. They were responsible for their
own judgments, their own decisions, their own acts. It helps us
to understand the wide social ramifications of violence if we realize
that from the highest echelons down, the psychiatrists acted spon-
taneously, without being forced.

A court in Coblenz probed this question most carefully in the case of three hospital psychiatrists who were charged with "aid to murder in an indefinite number of cases": "They have taken this task upon themselves voluntarily, just as altogether the collaboration in the 'action' was voluntary throughout." This is borne out by a letter from Himmler, chief of the SS, in response to an inquiry by a high judge: "What happens in the place in question [a psychiatric institution] is carried out by a commission of physicians. . . . The SS furnish only help in vehicles, cars, etc. The medical specialist, expert and responsible, is the one who gives the orders." In this connection the statement of Dr. Hans Hefelmann, an agronomist who was a highly placed bureaucrat in the "euthanasia" program, is significant. He made it in the abortive "euthanasia" trial at Limburg in 1964: "No doctor was ever ordered to participate in the euthanasia program; they came of their own volition." Other evidence confirms this.

What psychiatrists did made even members of the Nazi Party weep. When patients were transferred from their regular institution to one where they were to be killed, they were usually told that it was only a regular normal transfer from one hospital to another or that it was a change to a better place. Sometimes a glimpse of the truth would become known to patients, and scenes worthy of Callot or Goya would follow. Here is such a (true) scene. In the sleepy little town of Absberg, two large autobuses (belonging to a central transport agency of the "euthanasia" program) are parked on the street near an institution where there are several hundred mental patients. Some time before, twenty-five patients had been fetched by such a bus. Of these twenty-five, twenty-four "died" and one woman patient returned. The other patients in the institution learned what had happened, as did the inhabitants of the town. As the patients leave the institution to enter the buses, they are afraid, they refuse and remonstrate. Force is used by the personnel, and each patient is shoved violently into a bus. A large group of bystanders has assembled. They are so moved that they break into tears. The whole operation is presided over by an experienced psychiatrist from the big state hospital Erlangen. Among those spectators who cried openly at this pitiful spectacle were—as the official Nazi report states—"even members of the Nazi Party." There is no mention anywhere that doctors had any tears in their eyes.

To place causal responsibility on the physician does not in any way diminish the responsibility of the high and low Nazi officials and bureaucrats involved. But by the same token, placing full responsibility on these officials does not in the slightest diminish the role of the psychiatrist in the slaughter. In order to get the proper focus, we must think in terms of causal factors. If it takes two to plan and commit deliberate murder, that does not mean that only one is guilty. Even if the psychiatrists had been under orders, which they were not, it is noteworthy that their complete mobilization for killing patients went as speedily and as smoothly as the military mobilization of soldiers to fight the enemy.

Two "extenuating" circumstances, often claimed, have to be seriously weighed. One is that the psychiatrists did not know; the other is that very few were involved. In the very beginning, some psychiatrists may not have known what happened to their patients when they were transferred en masse in buses to other, unnamed institutions. But it is preposterous to assume that this ignorance could last after tens of thousands had been killed. The claim that only a few psychiatrists were involved is equally invalid. The lowest estimate is that there were "perhaps fifty" who participated. Even if this were a correct number (which it is not), among them were some of the most renowned and distinguished academic and hospital figures. Actually, the extent of the operation makes it inevitable that there were many more involved in Germany and in Austria, perhaps three or four times that many (not to speak of the many psychiatric nurses acting under the instructions of psychiatrists). Of course, the degree of participation varied. For example, in the internationally famous hospital of Gütersloh, the director and his staff did not "select" patients for annihilation. But they delivered the patients, without resistance or protest, to the guards and escorts who drove up for them in trucks. That is participating in murder too.

In July, 1939, several months before Hitler's note was written, a conference took place in Berlin in which the program to kill mental patients in the whole of Germany was outlined in concrete, final form. Present and ready to participate were the regular professors of psychiatry and chairmen of the departments of psychiatry of the leading universities and medical schools of Germany: Berlin, Heidelberg, Bonn, Würzburg. Historians of medicine and sociologists will have a lot of work to do to explain this. So far they have not stated the problem or even noted the fact. At a conference in Dresden in March, 1940, Professor de Crinis, of Berlin University, talked over the program with the chief psychiatrists of large public mental hospitals (state hospitals). The classification of mental disorders on which devoted physicians in all countries had worked for centuries was reduced to a simple formula: patients "not worthy to live" and patients "worthy to be helped." There was no opposition on the part of the physicians, every one of whom held a responsible position in the state-hospital system. Questions of ethics or the juridical aspects were not even mentioned. The only questions raised by the participants at the conference were how the project could be carried through most "practically and cheaply." For example, the transfer of patients from their original institution to one where they were to be killed was called "impractical" because it meant "wasting of gasoline." Mass graves, to be leveled later, were recommended as being an economical procedure.

For several years during the time of the program, psychiatrists held meetings every three months in Heidelberg under the chairmanship of the professor of psychiatry at the University of Heidelberg. At these conferences the ways to conduct the extermination action were studied, and suitable measures were suggested to assure its efficacy.

The whole project is a model of the most bureaucratic mass murder in history. It functioned as follows. In the preparatory meetings the chief psychiatric experts of the project worked out the criteria by which patients should be selected. Questionnaires were prepared with questions as to diagnosis, duration of stay in the institution, and so on. In October, 1939, the first questionnaires went out to state hospitals and other public and private institutions where mental patients, epileptics, the mentally retarded, and other handicapped persons were taken care of. Copies of each filled-out questionnaire were sent to four psychiatric experts, who indicated with a + or — their opinion about whether the patient was to live or die. (No expert gave an opinion on questionnaires filled out for patients in his own institution, but only on those of other institutions. Therefore he had no personal knowledge whatsoever of the patients.) This typical correspondence shows that the psychiatric experts worked very hard.

Letter from the "euthanasia" central office in Berlin to Member of the Commission of Experts, dated November 25, 1940:

Enclosed I am sending you 300 report sheets [questionnaires] from the institution Lüneburg with the request for your expert opinion.
(Signed)

Answering letter from the Member of the Commission of Experts to the central office in Berlin, dated November 29, 1940:

Enclosed I am sending you the 107th batch of report sheets, namely, 300 sheets complete with my expert opinion.
(Signed)

This rapid selection and certification of death candidates is not a record or by any means exceptional. The same expert formed his opinion on 2,190 questionnaires in two weeks and on 258 in two days.

The questionnaires with expert opinions indicated by the + or the — were then sent to a chief expert, who passed the final judgment. Beginning in January, 1940, the patients marked for death were transferred, directly or via intermediate stations, to the six psychiatric institutions in which gas chambers had been installed for the program. In these lethal institutions the patients were dealt with summarily and quickly, as this typical letter shows, from the social-welfare association Swabia to the director of the state hospital Kaufbeuren:

I have the honor to inform you that the female patients transferred from your hospital on November 8, 1940, all died in the month of November in the institutions Grafeneck, Bernburg, Sonnenstein, and Hartheim.
(Signed)

In some institutions, like Hartheim in Austria, things went so fast sometimes that it took only four hours from the time a patient was admitted till he left "through the chimney."

The backbone of the whole project was the experts. It was their decision which sealed the fate of every victim. Who were these men? That is the most remarkable part of the story—and the most important one for the future of violence and, I believe, of mankind. They were not nonentities or outsiders. Most of them had all the hallmarks of civic and scientific respectability. They were not Nazi puppets, but had made their careers and reputations as psychiatrists long before Hitler came to power. Among them were more than twelve full professors at universities. Most of their names read like a roster of prominent psychiatrists. They have made valuable contributions to scientific psychiatry. They are still quoted in international psychiatric literature, which testifies to their scientific stature. The bibliography of their papers, monographs, and books—not to mention their graduate and postgraduate lectures and their editorial work on leading psychiatric journals—would fill a whole brochure. We must make ourselves familiar with the caliber of these men if we want to comprehend the full meaning of this historical occurrence.

Dr. Max de Crinis was professor of psychiatry at the University of Berlin and director of the psychiatric department of the famous Charité Hospital. He was originally chief physician at the psychiatric clinic at the University of Graz. Those who knew him personally describe him as a "charming Austrian." He has many scientific studies to his credit, on alcoholism, epilepsy, war neuroses, pathology of the central nervous system (brain edema and brain swelling), etc. He was especially interested in the bodily concomitants of mental disorders—for instance, malfunction of the liver. Textbooks, including recent ones, refer to some of his scientific work as authoritative. In 1944, he published an interesting book on the somatic foundations of emotions which is still quoted in the scientific literature today. It is not easy to understand—but is important to know—how such a man could deliberately and personally, from his own department in the university hospital, send a thirteen-year-old boy afflicted with mongolism, with only minor mental impairment, to one of the murder institutions—the children's division of Goerden—to be killed. In 1945, when his car could not get through the Russian encirclement of Berlin, Dr. de

Crinis committed suicide with a government-supplied capsule of cyanide.

One of the most distinguished (and most unexpected) members of the team of experts which was the heart of the whole killing operation was Werner Villinger, who at the time was professor of psychiatry at the University of Breslau. Prior to that he was head of the department of child psychiatry at Tuebingen and then psychiatric director at Bethel, a world-famous institution for epileptics and mentally and physically disabled persons founded in 1867. From 1946 to 1956 he was professor of psychiatry at the University of Marburg. His clinical research on the outbreak of an acute psychosis after the commitment of a violent crime became well known. He wrote especially on the psychological and social difficulties of children and youths, on child guidance, group therapy, juvenile delinquency, and similar subjects. He has been decorated by the West German government. In 1950 he was invited to participate in the White House Conference on Children and Youth and did so.

His name alone, quite apart from his activity in it, gave a great boost to the "euthanasia" project. For his name suggested to others, especially younger psychiatrists, that there could be nothing wrong with the "action." It is difficult to understand how a man with concern for youths could not only consent to but actively participate in projects of killing them, but we may find some slight hints in his previous writings. Two years before Hitler came to power, Villinger advocated the sterilization of patients with hereditary diseases. Writing about the "limits of educability," he stated that "the deepest roots of what we call temperament and character are deep in the inherited constitution." Contrary to our modern point of view, he regarded the chances for the rehabilitation of juvenile delinquents with definite emotional difficulties as very poor.

During the preparation of the "euthanasia" trial in Limburg, Dr. Villinger was questioned by the prosecutor in three sessions. At about the same period, it became publicly known that he was implicated in the "euthanasia" murders in a leading, active role. He went to the mountains near Innsbruck and committed suicide. An attempt was made later to make this appear an accident, but there is no doubt about what happened.

To find Dr. Carl Schneider as a leading member of a wholesale murder project is also unexpected. For twelve years he was professor of psychiatry at the University of Heidelberg. As such he held the same important position as Emil Kraepelin a generation before. And Kraepelin was the founder of modern clinical psychiatry. In a recent textbook, Schneider's scientific work is referred to eleven times. In some of the most recent publications on the course of mental diseases and on the effect of tranquilizers, his clinical subdivisions are taken as a basis. He made clinical investigations of mental disorders in organic brain diseases and in pernicious anemia. He wrote on abnormal personalities in relation to diminished legal responsibility. Since experimental psychoses are currently much investigated, it is of interest that more than thirty years ago he induced an experimental psychosis in himself with mescaline. He described it in his monograph on hallucinations. One of his monographs deals with "The Treatment and Prevention of Mental Disorders." He studied epilepsy and expressed modern views about it, and his research on that subject is still quoted. He wrote two books on schizophrenia. The first, *The Psychology of Schizophrenia,* is considered a landmark of this type of clinical study. Originally more interested in subtle psychological analyses, he stressed more and more the hereditary factor.

Carl Schneider was very active in all phases of the program. He served as expert for the processing of death questionnaires, participated in the frequent conferences, and regularly instructed younger psychiatrists in the methods and procedures of the project. Perhaps the most extraordinary part of this story is that before going to Heidelberg, he, like Werner Villinger, had held the highly respected position of chief physician at the universally recognized institution Bethel. Ten years later, when he was professor at Heidelberg, he appeared with an SS commission at Bethel, went over the questionnaires, ordered the personnel to present patients to him, and personally selected the candidates for extermination. When, after the defeat of the Nazi regime, Dr. Schneider was to be put on trial, he committed suicide.

Another psychiatrist with an international reputation is Professor Paul Nitsche. He was successively director of several state hospitals, including the tradition-rich Sonnenstein in Saxony, which was the first psychiatric state hospital in Germany. In the authoritative *Handbook of Psychiatry* (1925–1932), he wrote the section on "Therapy of Mental Diseases," based on his own vast experience. He was one of the editors of the German *Journal for Mental Hygiene*. He wrote understandingly on modern psychotherapeutic measures in mental hospitals. He was interested in psychoses in prisoners (prison psychoses), and his book on the subject appeared in the best American monograph series on nervous and mental diseases. In the killing project he held a top position. He functioned as a representative of Dr. Brandt, the "leader" of the medical sector (as opposed to the strictly administrative bureau). He did his work of organizing and selecting death candidates so well that during the project he was advanced from expert to chief expert.

Nitsche presents perhaps the most remarkable psychological enigma. Colleagues of his who knew him well and who condemn him for his "euthanasia" work nevertheless say of him that he was "an exceptionally good psychiatrist, especially kind to his patients and concerned about them day and night." So can a false fanatical social orientation play havoc with a man's character. Here we come up against a contradiction which plays a great role in modern violence: the contrast in the same individual between the private, intimate, spontaneous personality and the corporate, public, official personality.

After the Nazi regime ended, Dr. Nitsche was tried in Dresden for the murder of mental patients and was sentenced to death. In 1947 he was executed.

Perhaps the greatest break with the humane traditions of psychiatry is connected with the name of Dr. Werner Heyde. Heyde was professor of psychiatry at the University of Würzburg and director of the psychiatric clinic there. Few places in the world can look back on such a long history of successful care of mental patients. The clinic grew out of a division of a general hospital where mental patients were admitted and kindly treated as early as the last decades of the sixteenth century. It is interesting that exactly contemporary with the extant case histories of this hospital are the descriptions by Cervantes in *Don Quixote* (first chapter of the second part) of the mental institution in Seville (around 1600).

Cervantes' stories of the inmates show that this institution (*casa de los locos*) was humanely administered. In other words, in two geographically widely separated and different localities, Seville and Würzburg, pioneer work was done that long ago in treating the mentally afflicted as human beings and as medical patients. It is certainly a problem for the historian of culture, as it is for the student of violence, that in the same place where mental patients were treated most humanely in 1583, they were doomed to be killed in 1940. In the later nineteenth and in the twentieth century, the Würzburg psychiatric clinic played a prominent role in scientific research. A number of outstanding psychiatrists got their training there. The first intelligence test was devised there in 1888. One of the earliest clinical observations and descriptions of what was later called schizophrenia came from that clinic.

Dr. Heyde's reputation as a scientic psychiatrist was excellent. He worked for several years in the clinic, became director of the out-patient department, and began his teaching there in 1932.

One of Heyde's predecessors as head of the Würzburg clinic, Conrad Rieger, who studied especially the history of psychiatry, wrote, almost prophetically, in his autobiography in 1929 (ten years before the start of the extermination program): "Whether it is deliberate or through negligence, it is wrong to kill human beings and to deprive them of care. On the contrary, we must care for them and protect them, well and humanely. This care and protection is needed in the same measure for the so-called curable and the so-called incurable." We do not know whether Heyde ever read this statement, which he so completely reversed. Heyde was a key figure in the program. When carbon monoxide was suggested as a method for killing, this proposal had to be submitted first to him for evaluation. He approved the method and directed the idea into the proper administrative channels for its practical realization. He was the head of one of the agencies of the project, the Reich Society for Mental Institutions (state hospitals). In his office the data from these institutions were collected and the last word pronounced about the patients to be sent to the special extermination hospitals. He played the leading role in the preparatory and organizing conferences (before Hitler's private note), helped in working out the questionnaires, functioned as chief expert, and selected the younger psychiatrists for the program and instructed them in their task.

From the beginning, he personally inspected the death institutions and the installation of the gas chambers, to make sure that everything functioned expeditiously. In addition, far from being told what to do, he gave lectures before high officials in the Nazi ministries to promote and explain the weeding out of those "not worthy to live." For example, on April 23, 1941, in the Department of Justice, he gave a lecture on "The Euthanasia Program" before high officials, judges, and prosecutors. The most important person present was the president of the highest court, the Reich Court, Judge Erwin Bumke. Bumke had been appointed to his office in 1929, during the democratic Weimar Republic. He raised no objection to the mass killing after this lecture, and the doom— the legal doom—of the mental patients was sealed. Psychiatry and law had met in the spirit of violence.

After the collapse of the Nazi regime, Heyde was arrested, but he escaped from custody. A warrant for his arrest ("Wanted for Murder . . ."), with his picture on it, was sent out. It said that he was probably working as a physician. For twelve years he lived a charmed existence under a different name. He was employed by a state insurance agency, again as chief expert. He did a great deal of work for courts. During this time his wife was receiving a widow's pension, and from money earned in his new career she bought a beautiful house on Lake Starnberg, near Munich. Many private persons—judges, prosecutors, physicians, university professors, and high state officials—knew his real identity. There was a certain solidarity in protecting this secret of violence. When his identity did come out, almost by accident, he surrendered to the authorities. His trial at Limburg was delayed for four years for preliminary investigation. He made another attempt to escape, which failed. When he was left unguarded in his cell five days before the trial was due to start, he committed suicide.

This trial, which would have been the most important "euthanasia" trial, delayed overlong, never took place. One day before Dr. Heyde's suicide, his codefendant, Dr. Friedrich Tillman, who from 1934 to 1945 was director of orphanages in Cologne and who has been called a "bookkeeper of death," jumped or was pushed from a tenth-story window. Another defendant, Dr. Gerhard Bohne, escaped from jail to South America. And the fourth defendant, Dr. Hefelmann, was declared not able to stand trial because of illness. The widely held belief that there was great pressure against this trial's taking place seems to be not without foundation.

Among other outstanding professors of psychiatry who were involved in the program were the following:

Dr. Berthold Kihn was the professor of psychiatry at the famous University of Jena, where Hegel, Fichte, Schiller, and Haeckel taught, where Karl Marx got his doctor's degree and the composer Schumann an honorary doctorate. He contributed chapters to several authoritative textbooks—for example, on neurosyphilis, on peripheral nerves, and on disorders of old age. He did research on the microscopic study of brain tissues. Kihn not only was busy making the death crosses on questionnaires, but also personally supervised the selection of patients for extermination in various institutions. He and Dr. Carl Schneider were among the charter members of one of the main project agencies.

Dr. Friedrich Mauz was professor of psychiatry at Koenigsberg from 1939 to 1945 and has held the same position at the University of Münster since 1953. A good deal of his scientific work became generally acknowledged: his studies on hysteria and epilepsy, with interesting clinical observations; on psychoses in juveniles; on the physical constitution in mental disorders. From him comes the term "schizophrenic catastrophe," for the most severe progressive types of the disease. In 1948 he participated as one of three official delegates from Germany at an international mental hygiene meeting in London. At that congress, the World Federation for Mental Health was founded, its purpose being the "furthering of good human relations."

Dr. Mauz excused himself later, without any condemnation of the "euthanasia" project, by saying that his invitation to a "euthanasia" conference in Berlin was "harmlessly formulated" and that as late as the autumn of 1940 (when tens of thousands of patients from all over Germany had been killed and whole hospitals closed because all the patients had been evacuated to death institutions), he, who held a responsible and administrative position in psychiatry, did not know anything about any "carrying through of the euthanasia program."

This list is far from complete.

In the whole "euthanasia" matter the universities, including the psychiatric and pediatric departments, wrapped themselves in silence. How easy it would have been (and riskless) to refuse, had anyone been so minded, is shown by the case of Gottfried Ewald, professor of psychiatry in Göttingen. He was invited to a conference at the central office in Berlin under the chairmanship of Heyde and was asked to join the program. He refused and left the conference. He remained unmolested and had no disadvantage on account of his complete refusal.

There is an interesting sidelight on his exceptional behavior. Among those whom the experts marked on the questionnaires or report sheets as "unworthy to live," and who were consequently killed, were veterans who had lost an arm or leg in the war. The records are clear about that. For example, among a group of male patients transferred from the state hospital Rottenmuenster to a death institution was one whose "euthanasia" questionnaire said: "Receives war pension. Handicapped for work through loss of an arm." Professor Ewald had lost his left arm in World War I and referred to it occasionally in his lectures. Maybe that made it easier for him to identify with the victims.

A young German psychiatrist of much lower rank, Dr. Theo Lang, made a serious attempt to stem the whole program. He was at that time in Germany and later became chief physician of the institution Herisau in Switzerland. On January 20, 1941, he obtained an interview with Dr. M. H. Goering at the German Institute for Psychological Research and Psychotherapy. His plan was to get Dr. Goering to sign a declaration against the extermination of mental patients. When he tried to tell Dr. Goering the whole story of the program, which at that time had been going on for more than a year, he found that Dr. Goering knew all about it and confirmed its truth. However, he refused to sign the declaration, and so nothing came of this *démarche*.

In taking this step—and for this reason his name should not be forgotten—Dr. Lang showed extraordinary courage. In going to Dr. Goering, he knew that he was approaching the very seats of

Nazi power, both political and psychiatric. Dr. Goering was a cousin of Marshal Hermann Goering, with whom he was in personal contact. And his close collaborator and coeditor on the Nazi-coordinated *Journal for Psychotherapy* for several years was Dr. C. G. Jung. Dr. Jung, in the words of the then State Secretary for Health, Dr. Conti, "represented German psychiatry under the Nazis." So Dr. Lang could not reach any higher with his plea for mercy and decency.

In addition to the professors of psychiatry, the experts included directors of large and well-known state hospitals from different parts of Germany, like Buch, near Berlin, and Eglfing, near Munich. They were also busy making the death crosses on the questionnaires and helping in other ways. These experts were not new appointees of the Nazi regime, but had had long and honorable careers. They were by no means products of Nazism, but were parallel phenomena. Their thinking was similar: the attacking of a social problem by violence. However well disguised by high-sounding terms like "eugenics" and "euthanasia," the problem was essentially economic and sociopolitical, namely, the cost of care for the temporarily "unproductive" and the prosperity and glory of the nation.

It is important to keep in mind that among those in responsible positions and most actively engaged in the killing were psychiatrists of ability. For example, Dr. Valentin Falthauser, director of a state hospital, was sentenced to three years in prison for practices that contributed to the death of three hundred hospital inmates. He was coauthor of an important book *Home Care in Psychiatry and Allied Fields,* which contains ideas which are still of great actuality for current community psychiatry.

The special agency for child "euthanasia," the Reich Commission for the Scientific Registration of Hereditary and Constitutional Severe Disorders, had as its most prominent expert Dr. Werner Catel, who was subsequently professor of pediatrics at the University of Kiel until the sixties. This was a commission of experts, psychiatric and pediatric, that decided—entirely on its own—which children should be killed as being mentally below par or handicapped or physically malformed. Dr. Catel still defends and advocates his type of "euthanasia" today—for instance, in his book *Borderline Situations of Life* (1962). It is a noteworthy fact for the recognition of the violence content of a democratic society that the head of a child-killing organization with thousands of victims should become the professor of pediatrics and head of a pediatric clinic at a renowned university.

The children slated for death were sent to special "children's divisions," first Goerden, then Eichberg, Idstein, Steinhof (near Vienna), and Eglfing. They were killed mostly by increasing doses of Luminal or other drugs either spoon-fed as medicine or mixed with their food. Their dying lasted for days, sometimes for weeks. In actual practice, the indications for killing eventually became wider and wider. Included were children who had "badly modeled ears," who were bed wetters, or who were perfectly healthy but designated as "difficult to educate." The children coming under the authority of the Reich Commission were originally mostly infants. The age was then increased from three years to seventeen years. Later, in 1944 and 1945, the work of the commission also included adults.

A further method of "child euthanasia" was deliberately and literally starving children to death in the "children's divisions." This happened to very many children. In most instances, these deaths were recorded as normal or natural deaths. But many people knew about the fact itself. As early as autumn 1939, a student of psychology, later a public-school teacher, Ludwig Lehner, was permitted with other visitors to go through the state hospital Eglfing-Haar. He went there as part of his studies in psychology. In the children's ward were some twenty-five half-starved children ranging in age from one to five years. The director of the institution, Dr. Pfannmueller, explained the routine. We don't do it, he said, with poisons or injections. "Our method is much simpler and more natural." With these words, the fat and smiling doctor lifted an emaciated, whimpering child from his little bed, holding him up like a dead rabbit. He went on to explain that food is not withdrawn all at once, but the rations are gradually decreased. "With this child," he added, "it will take another two or three days."

Surely this is a scene worse than Dante. But the punishment was anything but Dantesque. In 1948, Dr. Pfannmueller was specifically charged in court with having ordered the killing of at least 120 children and having killed some himself. It was testified that he had personally killed some of the children with injections. He was sentenced to six years in jail, of which he served two years. That makes about six days per killed child.

How great the professional moral confusion can become is evident from this sidelight. Professor Julius Hallervorden, a well-known neuropathologist, after whom a special brain disease is named (Hallervorden-Spatz disease), asked the central office of the program to send him the brains of "euthanasia" victims for his microscopic studies. While the victims were still alive, he gave instructions about how the brains should be removed, preserved, and shipped to him. Altogether he got from the psychiatric death institutions no less than six hundred brains of adults and children. It evidently did not occur to him, or to anybody else, that this of course involved him seriously in the whole proceeding. An American professor of psychiatry at a well-known medical school told a national magazine that there was no ethical problem involved here and that Dr. Hallervorden "merely took advantage of an opportunity."

By the middle of 1941, at least four of the death hospitals in Germany and Austria not only killed patients but became regular murder schools: Grafeneck, in Brandenburg; Hadamar, near Limburg; Sonnenstein, in Saxony; and Hartheim, near Linz. They gave a comprehensive course in lethal institutional psychiatry. Personnel were trained in the methods of assembly-line killing. They were taught the mass-killing techniques, "gassing," cremation, and so on. It was called basic training in "mercy killing." The "material" for all this training was mental hospital patients. On them the methods were tried out and tested before they were applied later to Jewish and other civilian populations of the occupied countries. Technical experience first gained with killing psychiatric patients was utilized later for the destruction of millions. The psychiatric murders came first. It is a revealing detail that a man named Gomerski, who was engaged in mass killing in the death camps of Sobibor and Treblinka, was nicknamed the Doctor because of his "euthanasia" training in the psychiatric hospital Hadamar.

The method of taking out gold fillings and gold teeth from victims was first tried, worked out, and routinely used on the mental-hospital patients killed. Only after that was it practiced on concentration-camp inmates. The patients had to open their mouths and a number was stamped on their chests. From this number the personnel knew which patients had gold teeth, so that they could be removed later. The first human-derived ingots of gold for the Reichsbank were made from the gold from the mouths of these mental patients. According to sworn testimony, several grams of gold meant several thousand people killed. In Berlin there was a special office, the Central Accounting Office, to keep track of the proceeds from killed mental patients. How to take gold teeth from the dead was taught as a special skill. For example, in the institution Hadamar, a man named Loeding had learned this "breaking of teeth," as it was called. Later he was transferred for this purpose to the institution Eichberg. All this was done in the name of euthanasia. Later it was applied to millions of people.

Toward the end of 1941 the gas chambers in the death institutions were dismantled, transported to the east, and there freshly erected for their new tasks in concentration camps. Meanwhile the killing of mental patients went on with other methods, with injections, for instance. "Only" a few thousand were now being killed each month.

Some of the same psychiatrists who selected patients in hospitals went to concentration camps and selected death candidates there. Himmler had the idea of having the inmates of these camps examined "to comb out" those to be eliminated. He needed suitable physicians. So the central bureau of the "euthanasia" program supplied him with "experienced psychiatrists." In practice, this worked out as follows. In 1941 a commission of five went to the concentration camp Dachau to select prisoners to be transferred to Mauthausen to be killed. All five men were psychiatrists, and their chief was a professor of psychiatry of the University of Berlin. As they sat at tables put up between two barracks, the inmates had to file past while the doctors looked at their records. The criteria for selection were set by two chief experts in psychiatry. They consisted in (*a*) ability to work and (*b*) political reports. Several hundred of the so-selected prisoners were sent to Mauthausen and destroyed there.

The director of the state hospital Eichberg, Dr. Fritz Mennecke, who went to concentration camps as expert to select death candidates, was asked in court about the two types of cases he had judged interchangeably, the mental patients on medical grounds and the camp prisoners on political grounds. "One cannot separate them," he answered. "They were not subdivided and neatly separated from each other."

The typical case of Dr. Adolf Wahlmann, psychiatrist at the state hospital Hadamar, shows how easy the change was for some psychiatrists from killing mental patients to killing foreign civilians. He was not a Nazi and not a sadist. He had had a good medical education in the universities of Giessen, Marburg, Erlangen, and Kiel and had worked for years in responsible psychiatric posts in different institutions. In the Hadamar institution, thousands of mental patients were killed. In 1944 shipments of Polish and Russian men, women, and children from other institutions and work camps in occupied territories were sent to Hadamar. They were killed by lethal injections which he prescribed, exactly as he had done before with mental patients.

There is a persistent myth about the whole "euthanasia" project which serves to ease the conscience of the civilized world. It is entirely false. According to this myth, Hitler stopped the program after about a year (when "only" some 70,000 patients had been killed) because of protests and pressure from the churches and the public. The "euthanasia" killing was *not* stopped. It went on until 1945, to the end of the Hitler regime—and in some places, *e.g.,* Bavaria, even a few days longer. There is no evidence that it was stopped; all the evidence is that it continued. It did not end; it merely changed its outer form. It did not even get less cruel but in many cases was more cruel. The killing was not done as before, in the form of conspicuous big actions, but was carried out in a more cautious form and at a slower pace. From 1941 on, instead of the gas chambers (which had been transferred), other methods were used. Without any formal procedure and without any norm, it was carried out by individual institutions and individual doctors. They selected, decided, and acted. The end effect was the same. The methods employed were deliberate withdrawal of food, poisoning, or in many cases a combination of both. The poisoning was done by injections of overdoses of drugs. Patients screaming from hunger were not unusual. If it got too bad, they were given injections which quieted them, made them apathetic, or killed them. This was called euthanasia too. "Euthanasia" by starvation. Such methods had the advantage of more discretion: patients who were destroyed in this way could be more easily counted as "natural deaths." It was the occupation by the Allied armies both in the north and in the south which freed the remaining patients from the psychiatrists.

Examples of continued general "mercy killings" after their alleged end in the summer of 1941 exist for every year thereafter, until 1945. At the end of 1942, at a conference of state officials and the directors of state hospitals, there was a discussion of the "excellent" method of making the "useless eaters" (*i.e.,* patients) die by "slow starvation." A hospital employee has reported that in 1940 she worked in one of the death-dealing hospitals; then she was transferred to another, where the patients were not killed with gas but with injections and overdoses of drugs; she worked there until 1943; she was sent to a third hospital, where the same procedures were used until the overthrow of the regime in 1945. The chief male nurse of one mental hospital described the progression. In 1940 the program started when mental patients were gassed to death and then burned. In 1941 the gassing was discontinued. Beginning in 1942 the patients were killed with lethal doses of morphine, scopolamine, Veronal, and chloral. In 1944 foreign slave laborers from the camp were also admitted to the hospital and killed in the same way. This account is entirely uncontested testimony and is typical for the whole project. In 1944 patients were still being transported from their hospitals to "special institutions" (to be killed) under the pretext that it was a regular routine transfer from one hospital to another.

With respect to children, the legend of the 1941 ending of "mercy deaths" does not have even a semblance of truth. The child-killing agency functioned openly and efficiently till the collapse of the regime in 1945. Nobody has claimed that it ended before. Under its auspices, the mass murder of children continued routinely all over Germany and Austria. In Vienna, for example— the golden Viennese heart notwithstanding—children were killed in the children's division of the famous institution Steinhof and the municipal children's institution Spiegelgrund until the end of the war. Professor I. A. Caruso, now well known for his book *Existential Psychology,* who as a young psychologist witnessed some of this himself, says of the Reich Commission that its "murderous activity" was "massive." It was also, as one writer put it, unbelievably cruel.

As for the Hitler "order" for the alleged termination of the project, no document existed, not even a private note as at the outset of the "action." What happened was that in the late summer of 1941 in his General Headquarters, in a conversation with his physician, Dr. Karl Brandt, Hitler asked for the "provisional cessation of the euthanasia action on a large scale." This was purely verbal and was not written. It was an organizational change. It was clearly foreshadowed in a previous statement by Gestapo chief Himmler that there were "faults in the practical procedures." (The killing with the gas installations was too conspicuous.) Soon after Hitler's talk with Dr. Brandt, the chief expert, Professor Heyde, made it very plain in a written communication that the change was merely a "technical matter." Indeed, the gas chambers were moved, but the killing in the mental institutions in Germany continued with other methods.

As for the resistance of the churches, the fact that the killing did continue shows that it was not so strong or so persistent as to be effective. It was not enough. Dr. Karl Brandt stated that it was Hitler's opinion (which proved right) that resistance to the "euthanasia" killings on the part of the churches would under the circumstances not play a great role. The efforts were sporadic, isolated, and fragmentary. At certain levels the attitude was for a long time so passive and ambiguous that a top bureaucrat in the mercy killings, Hans Hefelmann, could state truthfully in court in Limburg that it had been his understanding that the church "was willing to tolerate such killings [at the time] under certain conditions."

What clergymen did was sixfold. They first protested about the transfer and eventual killing of patients in institutions under their jurisdiction. They wrote to the government and submitted evidence. They protested against the project from the pulpit. In some, but not all, institutions where religious sisters worked as nurses, the clergy made the further work of the sisters dependent on the assurance that they did not *have* to "participate" in any way in any part of the project. They reported instances to local juridical authorities as punishable crimes. (This was of no effect, because all complaints relating to the "action" were forwarded to Berlin and disregarded.) Finally we know of at least one occasion when a prominent clergyman achieved a long personal interview with one of the officials of the program and pleaded with him. A highly respected pastor, Fritz von Bodelschwingh, the chief of the Bethel institution, invited Dr. Karl Brandt to visit Bethel. Dr. Brandt accepted and the two men conferred for three hours.

It was a memorable event. Dr. Karl Brandt was a complex personality. He knew Dr. Albert Schweitzer well, was impressed with his theory of "reverence for life" and interested in his philanthropic work. As a young doctor he had planned to work with him as an assistant in Lambaréné in Africa. The only reason why that did not come about was that Brandt was born in Alsace and the French would have called him up in Lambaréné for military service. We can speculate that his whole career might have been different—in fact, might have taken just the opposite direction—if social preparation for war and violence had not prevented it. From what Pastor Bodelschwingh related later of their talk, Dr. Brandt tried to explain that the "euthanasia" project was necessary to save the nation. Bodelschwingh's position was that nobody has the right to be inhuman to his fellowmen. It seems that as a result of this discussion the liquidation of the "not worthy to live" inmates of Bethel was at least postponed and it may have helped many to escape this fate.

On March 8, 1941, the Catholic bishop Clemens von Galen of Münster, in Westphalia, spoke from the pulpit against the "euthanasia" action. He said: "These unfortunate patients must die because according to the judgment of some doctor or the expert opinion of some commission they have become 'unworthy to live' and because according to these experts they belong to the category of 'unproductive' citizens. Who, then, from now on could still have confidence in a physician?" This sermon helped to inform the public further but it had no lasting effect. For it was only a one-shot condemnation, not followed up by the bishop, not reinforced by higher dignitaries of the church, and not backed by Rome. (Von

Galen died a Cardinal in 1946.) The forces of destruction and propaganda had become so entrenched that the public could no longer do anything about it anyhow.

Why, then, in 1941 was the program changed in methods, speed, and conspicuousness? From the historical context of events and opinions, it is abundantly clear why Hitler interfered. He was concerned, and rightly so, with military morale. Would the spirit of the troops hold out to see the war through? It was late summer of 1941. Soldiers were learning that at home Germans were killing Germans. They were afraid that the wounded with head injuries would be sent to the gas chambers—and this might well happen to them. So the gas chambers were conspicuously dismantled. Moreover, going home on leave they might find that a grandparent or other aged relative had disappeared. Morale became affected, so it was more or less officially given out that the program was stopped. In reality it continued, but less blatantly than before.

In June, 1945, the American Military Government, through its Public Health and Security officers, investigated the psychiatric institution Eglfing-Haar, on the outskirts of Munich. In this hospital, some 300 children, from six months to sixteen years old, and about 2,000 adult patients had been killed on a thoroughly organized basis. This went on until the American occupation. Some of the adult patients had not been killed in the place itself but had been sent to an institution at Linz for killing and cremation. There were, at the very minimum, thirty such hospitals in Germany with "special departments" for destroying patients.

In Eglfing-Haar, which had had an excellent reputation as a psychiatric hospital, there was a children's division with a capacity of about 150 children called the *Kinderhaus*. This division had a "special department" with twenty-five beds and cribs for the children about to be exterminated. In June, 1945, it was still occupied by twenty children. They were saved by the American Army. In the children's "special department" there was a small room. It was bare except for a small white-tiled table. At the window was a geranium plant which was always carefully watered. Four or five times a month a psychiatrist and a nurse took a child to this little room. A little while later they came out, alone.

The killing of children was carried out by different methods.

One was overdoses of Luminal given either by injection or as a powder sprinkled over food. Another method was injection of a drug called modiscope, a combination of morphine, dionine, and scopolamine. Some children were given iodine injections with the result that they died in convulsions. Among the victims were retarded children who could have been taught and have led well-adjusted lives. Some were emotionally disturbed children who could not play well with other children and were regarded as "antisocial." The brains of the murdered children were sent to a psychiatric research institution for scientific microscopic studies.

The killing of adults was done almost entirely by deliberate starvation. The patients were given only vegetables and water until they died. They never got bread or meat or anything else. In this "special department," until the American Military Government took over, no patient got any treatment whatsoever, mental or physical. If he cut himself, he was not bandaged and was allowed to bleed. The selection of the patients to be put into this "special department" was largely in the hands of the staff psychiatrists and was a matter of routine. One criterion for selection was the length of stay in the institution. The whole procedure was known to all the hospital personnel.

We are still in the postviolence phase of the "euthanasia" murders. That is perhaps one of the darkest spots of the story. For the whole action has been minimized and left in a cloud of obfuscation, concealment, and social forgetfulness. We read about errors where there really was precision, about excesses where there were regular procedures, about dictates where there was all too ready compliance, about "misunderstood humaneness" where there was routine inhumanity. This happens not only in popular literature, but also in the writings of leading professional men.

To some extent, the courts have contributed to the confusion, which in its turn breeds indifference. For what were identical or very similar crimes, the sentences were of the greatest imaginable variety. A very few of those involved were sentenced to death and either executed or given death sentences which were commuted to life imprisonment and then reduced further; many were pardoned; in a number of cases, the courts decided that there was no case and no occasion for a trial; many were acquitted or received relatively short jail sentences; most remained entirely unmolested by the law and continued their professional or academic careers.

In some instances, the courts have made general statements about the project which tend to minimize its wrongfulness. For example, a court in Munich decided that "the extermination of mental patients was not murder, but manslaughter." In this summary form, which has been quoted in newspapers and magazines, the statement might give some people the dangerous idea that killing one person may be murder, but killing many is just manslaughter.

The reasons the courts have given for leniency or acquittal are revealing:

A court in Cologne, in acquitting one of the physicians, spoke of the victims, the patients, as "burned-out human husks." In another court opinion, the patients are called "poor, miserable creatures."

The director of a psychiatric hospital which served as an "intermediate institution" had accepted patients and then sent them on to death institutions with full knowledge of their eventual fate. The court gave as one reason for his acquittal that his role "does not represent an acceleration of the process of destruction, but a delay, and therefore a gain of time [for the patients]."

The director of a state hospital was acquitted on the ground that the many patients in whose death he was instrumental would have perished anyhow.

In a number of cases, the courts acted as if to kill or not to kill was a metaphysical question, like "to be or not to be." They quote the "ethics of Plato and Seneca" or speak of a "tragic conflict of duties" (acquittal in both cases).

Classic is the judgment of a Frankfurt court about a psychiatrist who not only killed many patients—adults and children—personally, but also watched their death agonies through the peep window of the gas chambers. "We deal," said the court, "with a certain human weakness which does not as yet deserve moral condemnation."

In the same way, in the case of a pediatric clinic in Hamburg where many children were deliberately killed ruthlessly, a medical organization proclaimed that the "actions of the inculpated female and male physicians in the years from 1941 to 1943 under the circumstances obtaining at that time did not represent any serious moral transgressions." And a medical journal stated that no professional action was indicated (such as depriving the physicians of their right to practice or to work in hospitals) because after the murders "their work in their profession was beyond reproach."

There has been—and still is—a great reluctance to face the whole "euthanasia" project as what it really was. We are concerned that the truth may damage the image of psychiatry (and pediatrics). But is not the substance more important than the image? A successful effort has been made to hush the whole thing up, in a cloud of silence, distortion, abstract speculations about life and death, irrelevant discussions of the duties of the doctor, and wholly irrelevant misuse of the term "euthanasia." In a recent book by a physician, Professor de Crinis is praised as a "courageous and energetic physician." The book *Euthanasia and Destruction of Life Devoid of Value* (1965), by the present professor of forensic and social psychiatry at the University of Marburg, speaks of the "comparatively few [*sic*] mental patients" killed. (This book is highly recommended in a recent number of an American psychiatric journal.)

In 1950 the then director of the state hospital Bernburg wrote an article in a scientific psychiatric journal in celebration of the seventy-fifth anniversary of that institution's beginning. In Bernburg more than 60,000 people had been murdered, the psychiatric director during that time having been a willing tool of the "euthanasia" project. The anniversary article speaks three times of the "reputation of the institution" as if that were the main point and calls the period of the mass killing an "episode and a step backwards" comparable to the (unavoidable) disruption of the service in the First World War.

This is violence unresolved. The psychiatric profession, to the limited extent that it has spoken at all, claims that the "euthanasia" murders were "ordered" by the Nazis. The record shows that is not true. But even supposing it were true, can we accept the position that if a political party "orders" the psychiatric profession to murder most of its patients, it is justified in doing so?

A recent trial in Munich throws light on several aspects of both the action phase and the postviolence phase of the "euthanasia" murders. What was established there was entirely typical. Tried for participation in murder were fourteen nurses of the psychiatric state hospital Obrawalde-Meseritz in which at least 8,000 mental patients (including children) were killed. This killing went on until 1945. The nurses gave lethal doses of drugs to the patients. The staff psychiatrists, male and female, selected the patients who were to be killed, prescribed the lethal doses, and ordered the killing. Once, in the beginning, when a nurse refused to give a deadly dose of Veronal (barbital) to a woman patient, the female chief psychiatrist gave her a "big bawling out." The defense of the nurses was that "we had to bow to the orders of the physicians." Routinely two or three patients were killed every day; in 1945 the number was increased to four a day. On the weekends there was no killing; it was a matter of "never on Sunday." After the end of the Nazi regime, most of the fourteen nurses continued in their regular professional work in hospitals as before. Three were working as nurses in hospitals at the time of the trial. All fourteen were acquitted. It was a triumph for the Goddess of Violence.

We are not dealing here with just the behavior of individual practitioners or professors or with just an accident in the practice of a science. What confront us are crucial problems in the relation of science and medicine to society and politics, of the value of human life versus national and social policy. We can learn what Dr. Richard Madden, a physician and social historian of "fanaticisms," wrote a hundred years ago, that behind all the veneer there is still "a great deal of savagery in the heart's core of civilization."

Bibliography

On Euthanasia

DEATH WITHOUT DIGNITY, Killing for Mercy, P. Marx. (Collegeville, MN) $0.90. Paperback, 46 pages.
  The best concise discussion of the relationship between abortion and euthanasia.
HANDBOOK ON EUTHANASIA, R. Sassone. (Available from Hayes Publishing Co.) $1.75 p.p. Paperback, 144 pages.
  Transcript of Senate hearing on "Death with Dignity" bill with other additional information.

DEATH, DYING AND EUTHANASIA, Horan and Mall. (Americans United for Life, 230 N. Michigan Avenue, Suite 515, Chicago, IL 60601) $8.00. Paperback, 817 pages.
A comprehensive treatment of the entire field.

THE "RIGHT TO KILL" AND THE THIRD REICH, R. Graham. Catholic Historical Review, Vol. LXII, No. 1, January, 1976.

THE RELEASE OF THE DESTRUCTION OF LIFE DEVOID OF VALUE, R. Sassone, (LIFE, 900 N. Broadway, Suite 725, Santa Ana, CA 92701) $1.50. Paperback, 112 pages.
A small book which bears a specific share of the blame for the ideas and values that fostered the German Euthanasia Program.

On Abortion

HANDBOOK ON ABORTION, B. and J. Willke, rev. ed., 1975. (Hayes Publishing Co.) $1.90 p.p. Paperback, 208 pages.
This "bible" of the pro-life movement is the most widely used book in the world presenting the scientific case for the unborn. Question and answer format, over 200 scientific papers quoted.

ABORTION, THE BIBLE AND THE CHRISTIAN, D. Shoemaker, 1976. (Hayes Publishing Co.) $1.25 p.p. Paperback, 62 pages.
A simple but thorough examination of what the Bible teaches on this subject.

ABORTION AND SOCIAL JUSTICE, T. Hilgers and D. Horan, 1972. (Sheed and Ward, available from Hayes Publishing Co.) $4.50 p.p. Paperback, 238 pages.
Treats in much greater depth (than *Handbook on Abortion*) the broad sweep of the abortion controversy.

ABORTION IN PERSPECTIVE, D. DeMarco, 1975. (Hayes Publishing Co.) $3.35 p.p. Paperback, 194 pages.
New philosophic insights. Breaks new ground in exploring the thinking we should be doing.

THE MORALITY OF ABORTION, LEGAL AND HISTORICAL PERSPEC- TIVES, J. Noonan, 1970. (Harvard University Press) $8.95. Cloth.
Excellent, logical, historically accurate, well balanced. Chapters by theologians, historians, and legal experts.

Related Subjects

CARE OF THE DYING, R. Lammerton. (Available from Hayes Publishing Co.) $2.00 p.p. Paperback, 160 pages.
An excellent description of England's Hospice program.

U.S. SUPREME COURT DECISIONS ON ABORTION: Roe vs. Wade, Doe vs. Bolton, 1973. (Available through your attorney or from Cincinnati Right to Life, P. O. Box 24073, Cincinnati, OH 45224). $2.00 p.p.

POPULATION GROWTH, C. Clark, 1972. (Available from Hayes Publishing Co.) $2.00 p.p. Paperback, 108 pages.
If you have read Ehrlich's *Population Bomb,* you should also read this almost total refutation by this world famous demographer.